The Bloomsbury Artists
Prints and Book Design

The Bloomsbury Artists

Prints and Book Design

catalogue by Tony Bradshaw

introduction by James Beechey
with a foreword by Angelica Garnett

SCOLAR PRESS

Copyright © Scolar Press 1999

Published by
Scolar Press
Gower House
Croft Road
Aldershot
Hants GU11 3HR
England

Ashgate Publishing Company
131 Main Street, Burlington
Vermont 05401
USA

First published 1999

ISBN 1 85928 277 6

British Library Cataloguing in Publication Data

A CIP record for this book is available from
the British Library

Reprinted 2000

Produced for the publisher by
John Taylor Book Ventures
Faringdon, Oxfordshire
Designed by Alan Bartram
Typeset by Tom Knott
Mears Ashby, Northampton
Printed in Singapore

For   Frances

And for   Peter
               Neil
               Mark

Contents

Foreword
Angelica Garnett

Drawing and painting was one of Vanessa Bell's preferred ways of communicating with children largely because, under her guidance, it became a shared activity. In the large cavernous room which did duty for a nursery in Gordon Square my mother drew a poodle, showing me how, by endowing him with pale green shadows and surrounding him with a sea of black, to make him look as white as snow. There was no chiaroscuro, simply a contrast of child-like simplicity, resembling the cut out of animals she did for the Omega nursery in 1913.

Showing the same intense desire to share the lives of her children, her own mother also had written stories for them in which there were no baddies – only goodies – a feeling shared by Vanessa that children should have only nice things to think about. In her illustrations for Julia Stephen's stories, done much later in life, there are no shadows and no perspective – nothing to suggest ogres, enchanted castles or nightmares.

It was no doubt from her father, who drew life-like animals in the margins of his books, that she inherited her gift for getting a likeness, either animal or human. But she rejected Leslie Stephen's facility in order to find her own personal way, visually uncompromising and remote, yet evoking a world of sensuality where the sun always shines and the shadows are filled with colour. If the designs lacked the drama usually associated with the art of illustration – showing more affinity with Gaugin than with Daumier – they succeeded in transcending the literal, creating a poetic parallel to the text which inspired her.

It was in Gordon Square that she gave me the memorable lesson in black and white, and there too that she probably did at least some of the designs for the Hogarth Press books. These too share the disarming simplicity of my poodle. I associate them with moments when, her mind at ease, she sat before the stove with a sketch book on her knee. If easel painting was a morning activity, conducted in the studio, designing for the page was destined for the lamp-lit evenings.

It was often a pleasure snatched from a moment which might otherwise have been given over to seeing friends or acquaintances such as Ethel Walker or Ethel Sands who were never asked to what Virginia Woolf called a 'meat meal', but only came to tea to be offered buttered toast and talk about current exhibitions and mutual friends with a Vanessa who, although she rather enjoyed it, would have greatly preferred to feel the softness of her black pencil rubbing against the grain of her paper. Struggling to find the essential but fugitive image was a far more satisfactory way of spending the time between tea and dinner.

It was not entirely unsociable either, since there were people, such as Duncan and myself, with whom at the same time Vanessa could carry on a desultory and laconic conversation about quite other things. At such moments Leonard Woolf, as the link between artist and printer, often came in for it. Bulwark as he was, it was dangerous to disagree with him, but impossible for Vanessa to disguise her irritation when he or his printer changed the position of a word, thus altering the whole design, or failed to appreciate the difference between Indian or Venetian red. Leonard then became something like a fetish into whom Vanessa stuck her pins of frustrated irritation.

The Hogarth Press books were meant for the common reader and not, for example, like those of the Nonesuch Press, intended to be lasting objects of beauty something that, because of what seemed to her excessive self-consciousness, Vanessa would have found unpalatable. Far from designing for future generations she concentrated on the moment, searching for spontaneity, consigning it to poor quality paper and simple line block printing which exactly suited her gift for the abstract and purely visual.

Duncan also sat in a chair to draw, but did it in the light of day rather than in the somnolent quiet of evening. Not sharing Vanessa's qualms with regard to fine paper and impeccable bindings, he did produce some designs for the Nonesuch, in which his friend David Garnett was a partner. His drawings were witty, calligraphic and light hearted, delighting his many literary friends. His inspiration was more closely related to the text than Vanessa's, less poetic but more lively – a vitality that lost a little of its vivacity in the printing since he found it more difficult than she did to accept the flatness of the printer's block. He was, I remember, very thrilled when Jack Beddington commissioned a poster for Shell on a large scale where, because printing had become more sophisticated, Duncan's designs could more closely resemble easel pictures. His rendering of the bridge at St Ives, near David Garnett's house in Huntingdonshire, was a fine example. When I lived there a copy of it hung in one of the bedrooms.

Technically Vanessa and Duncan were both amateurs without any training in the necessary procedures of printing, etching or lithography. They envied the French painter's collaboration with the famous printers of Paris, or their friends Pierre Clairin and his wife Line who, being specialists, had their own press and worked together to produce whole series of small wood or lino cuts which they sent us at Christmas. When, during the war, the so-called 'Ladies of Millers' turned up and started printing lithographs Duncan and Vanessa were entranced by the possibilities, although of course expected to pay for them by responding to innumerable invitations to intimate talks over lunch or tea.

Mrs Byng Stamper and her sister, Caroline Lucas, known as Mouie, were indeed an unexpected phenomenon, having descended, like autumn leaves, from a higher social sphere in which they had been fostered, protected and no doubt loved by Queen Victoria's granddaughter, Princess Marie Louise. In their home 'Millers' in Lewes it seems they found their own metier and branched out into numerous artistic or philanthropic activities, all of which, at that time foreign to the natural climate of Lewes, nonetheless prospered. Needless to say, in time of war, this was an immense boon, boosting the morale of artists and discovering a new and so far undetected public longing, in the prevailing gloom, for both education and amusement.

Duncan was of course the jewel in their crown and very willing to be so. For him their courtly manners and refined luncheon parties held no terrors. He would put on his spongebag trousers and a bow tie and drive into Lewes in the battered Morris, always hoping, at the very least, to bring descriptions and stories for our delight. Mouie's artistic aspirations, even her affinities with Barbara Hepworth, were only to be encouraged. The odd thing was that one could not imagine where or when in a life led under the aegis of Princess Louise, Barbara Hepworth could have come into it – although, now I come to think of it, it is quite likely that Princess Louise was an enlightened patron of the arts. It was an acknowledged fact, however, that Mouie, with her porcelain skin and slender wrists, actually wielded a hammer and chisel and sculpted pieces of marble into shapes that recalled both Hepworth and Brancusi. One of these stood for many years on the brink of the pond at Charleston, gently defended by Duncan from the supercilious remarks of the rest of us.

It was, I think, their ladylikeness – the very thing that Vanessa found most difficult to cope with – that ensured their extraordinary success. How could their iron grip, encased as it was in such a velvet glove, be refused any help they asked for? Bay Byng Stamper was the more obviously human of the two. She had a past, with a husband and a tragedy – a son, I think, who had drowned. Transparently maternal and benevolent, she spoke with inhibited dignity, like an Egyptian mummy scarcely unwrapped from her bandages. She and the nervous Mouie, dressed in brighter colours, dropped their Gs, and left out whole syllables in what was then thought of as a very upper-class fashion, and which branded them as non-intellectuals – noted with approval no doubt by the bourgeosie of Lewes, though less favourably by Vanessa.

Their true gift however was flair. They were perhaps the nearest the English could come to those ladies of America who make a superb collection of art and who often seem, by comparison with the reality of Monet or Cézanne, as insubstantial as penny plain or tuppence coloured. It was this surprising contrast which endowed Bay and Mouie with mystery and fascination. Sadly, the war over, they spent their last years in Shelley's Hotel in Lewes, dying without renown.

Like fish in muddy waters, memories elude command, some rapidly fading while others, such as the Ladies of Millers, come to the fore. I hope to be forgiven for welcoming them, since I must be the only person now alive who remembers them in this context. Their selfless, if somehow incongruous, devotion to the arts – and to Duncan in particular – should not go unrecognised. In their very different way they continued the tradition of the Omega, and in providing Duncan and Vanessa with the opportunity to print lithographs also gave them a link with a new public.

A catalogue of the prints and book jackets produced by the Bloomsbury artists has long been needed. Knowing Tony Bradshaw as I do, I feel sure that it will be impeccably done and wish the book all the success it undoubtedly deserves.

Introduction

James Beechey

The four artists whose graphic work is catalogued and illustrated in the pages that follow – Roger Fry, Vanessa Bell, Duncan Grant and Dora Carrington – are usually designated by the label 'Bloomsbury'; saddled with it, some would say. Bloomsbury was never an artistic movement; nor even was it an exhibiting society, like other groups that flourished at the beginning of the century and which also took their names from districts of London – Fitzroy Street, Camden Town and Cumberland Market. Bloomsbury was the denomination given to a group of intimate friends, drawn together through university and family connections, who from 1905 gathered at the house in Gordon Square shared by Thoby and Adrian Stephen and their two sisters: Vanessa, who married Clive Bell, one of Thoby's friends from Cambridge, and Virginia, who married another, Leonard Woolf. Many of them later followed the Stephens to Gordon Square, where they lived within a few doors of each other, or they took addresses in adjacent squares on the Bedford estate. The term was first applied, flippantly, within this circle; later it gained common currency among both their champions and detractors and with journalists; and more recently, it has been used (or, rather, abused) indiscriminately to describe almost anyone in intellectual London between the wars. As well as the artists and the critic Clive Bell, Bloomsbury embraced three of the great figures of the day, and of the modern period, in literature – Virginia Woolf, E. M. Forster and Lytton Strachey – and the pre-eminent one in economics – Maynard Keynes. Bloomsbury was identified with certain attitudes to aesthetics and literature, politics and war, and with various public enterprises in the arts. It was associated with the promotion of the two post-impressionist exhibitions at the Grafton Galleries in 1910 and 1912 which Roger Fry conceived and with the organisation of which Desmond MacCarthy, Clive Bell and Leonard Woolf all helped; with the Omega Workshops, the design studio of which Fry, Vanessa Bell and Duncan Grant were co-directors; and with the Hogarth Press, the publishing house founded by Leonard and Virginia Woolf, which commissioned work from each of the artists who are the subject of this book.

So much for a name. But was there any such thing as a Bloomsbury style of art? – or is it quite as idiotic to refer to one as it is to talk of a Bloomsbury method of writing, a Bloomsbury school of economic thought or a Bloomsbury practice of gardening? Roger Fry did not paint like Vanessa Bell or Duncan Grant, and no one could mistake a picture of his for one by Carrington. Bell and Grant are almost always coupled together. They lived and worked alongside each other for half a century, collaborated on numerous schemes of interior decoration (they were, in Virginia Woolf's phrase, 'the firm of Bell and Grant') and frequently painted in front of the same motif. But even their styles cannot easily be confused. Their artistic personalities were very different: Bell's grave, even severe; Grant's lyrical and fantastic. They both adopted a calligraphic shorthand (especially in their decorative work), but their particular handwriting is always recognisable. If it is fanciful to imagine a specifically Bloomsbury idiom, it is not incorrect to recognise a shared approach to making art. They delighted in the handmade. They revelled in spontaneity, cornucopian imagery and, for a time, a riot of colour. They gave not a jot for decorum, and readily put blue sheep on a screen, vermilion goldfish on a table-top and a recumbent nude inside the lid of a Dolmetsch virginal. (This ought not to imply, as is sometimes supposed, that they were slapdash.) Above all, they were extraordinarily versatile. They refused to accept the edges of a canvas as the natural bounds of their creativity: they designed sets and costumes, rugs and stuffs, they painted on ceramics and furniture, door-panels, walls and ceilings. Fry achieved a plan for decorating a London polytechnic; Bell and Grant produced murals for a primary school, a country church and a luxury liner; Carrington made signboards for pubs, and paintings on glass to sell in a local antiques shop. These all arose from a belief in a democratic art, un-pretentious and easily accessible. (Even at the age of ninety, Grant was producing lithographs to be sold through *The Observer* newspaper.) The artists themselves accepted a very broad definition of art, and the compiler of this catalogue has allowed a similar latitude in outlining their graphic work. There are listed here not just prints – primarily woodcuts and lithographs – and posters, book-jackets and illustrations, but also more prosaic items, often made at the request of friends: magazine covers, bookplates, menu cards, a honey label and a wedding invitation.

In dismantling the barriers between high and applied art, as in much else, Roger Fry was the driving force. He was a generation older than his Bloomsbury friends, and belonged to a more austere nineteenth-century tradition. Before he was forty he had become a figure of some distinction. He had made a reputation writing and lecturing on the early Italian Renaissance; he had been a curator at the Metropolitan Museum in New York and been offered the directorship of the National Gallery in London; and he was a principal member of the

New English Art Club. His own paintings were carefully constructed pastiches of the Old Masters. Nothing in them – or in the designs he contributed to books by two close friends, some spidery drawings and a frontispiece for C. R. Ashbee's *From Whitechapel to Camelot* and several Italianate *chiaroscuro* illustrations and the title page for R. C. Trevelyan's *Polyphemus and Other Poems* – suggest that his interests were any more up-to-date than those of the typical late Victorian. So, when in the autumn of 1910 Fry launched an initial assault on the English notion of polite taste with his exhibition of Manet and the Post-Impressionists, he shocked his old friends, outraged the public and perhaps surprised even himself. Earlier that year he had met Clive and Vanessa Bell on a train journey between Cambridge and London, and soon afterwards he was brought to Gordon Square. Fry quickly recruited his new allies in Bloomsbury to his campaign to stir up the parochial London art world, and in the Bells and Duncan Grant he found willing lieutenants. After brief spells at the Royal Academy and Slade Schools, Vanessa Bell had founded the Friday Club, which held lectures and debates as well as occasional exhibitions; Duncan Grant, back from a year studying in Paris, was one of its more regular contributors. Both had also sent pictures to the New English Art Club: now they were swept, all of a sudden, into an exhilarating confrontation with modern art. They were included in an English group, selected by Clive Bell, at the Second Post-Impressionist Exhibition in 1912 – for which Duncan Grant drew a poster, also used in a reduced form on some versions of the catalogue. A fashionable lady, drawn in a semi-cubist outline, looks in horror at the announcement of the exhibition.

By 1913, when Fry opened the Omega Workshops at 33 Fitzroy Square, even ladies of fashion had been converted to Post-Impressionism. Lady Cunard and Lady Ottoline Morrell, as well as the wives of the German and Belgian ambassadors and of General Sir Ian Hamilton, were all to be found at the Omega, buying screens and chairs, pottery and textiles, necklaces, hats, fans, parasols and opera bags – and marvelling at their gaudy colours and gauche designs. The Omega was established as a co-operative: the time any artist could spend in the workshops was limited to three half-days a week and the work they made there was sold anonymously. Even so, after the early defections of Wyndham Lewis and his Vorticist cohorts, its operations were controlled by a troika of Fry, Bell and Grant. But a host of young artists found temporary employment at the Omega, including many who became better-known after the war – and two, Paul Nash and Edward McKnight Kauffer, who later emerged as outstanding graphic artists. And a posse of young female helpers, several of them recent students at the Slade, made themselves indispensable in the showrooms and studios (especially after the call-up of most of the artists, and the removal from London of those others who were conscientious objectors). They put on post-impressionist tunics, some dropped the use of their Christian names, and they all wore their hair bobbed; Virginia Woolf christened them 'the cropheads'. One of these was Carrington, who entered the Slade just as Fry's first exhibition was provoking a great hullabaloo. Although she admitted at once to admiration for Cézanne, her own painting owed more to the influence of Augustus John and his acolytes in Chelsea – as well as to a native tradition of popular art – than to the insistent formalism preached in Bloomsbury. In her short life it was known only to a few friends and amateurs. She never showed her work publicly. She was a persistent artist, impatient to snatch any opportunity to paint or decorate, but she devoted as much energy during her last fifteen years to keeping house for Lytton Strachey.

It is likely that Fry had envisaged the production of illustrated books as one of the Workshops' activities at its outset; but it was not until 1915, when paper shortages occasioned much less propitious circumstances, that he began to make plans for an Omega imprint. The following year he published two slight volumes: a satirical poem *Simpson's Choice* by Arthur Clutton-Brock, art critic of *The Times* and a friend of Fry's, and *Men of Europe*, his own translation of a selection of poems on the horrors of war by the French writer Pierre-Jean Jouve. Both were decorated with woodcuts by Roald Kristian. Kristian was born Edgar de Bergen in Norway in 1893; he met Nina Hamnett in Paris in 1914 and married her later that year in London where they both worked at the Omega. An exhibition of Kristian's woodcuts was held there in 1915, but his career in England ended abruptly in 1917 when he was arrested as an unregistered enemy alien and deported. Fry's own interest in woodcuts had been stimulated by Eric Gill: he had commissioned a Christmas card from Gill in 1910 and he tentatively cut cards himself in 1911 and 1913. He may also have gained inspiration for his publishing projects (as Judith Collins has suggested) from the Parisian dealer Ambroise Vollard, who had lent several paintings to the Second Post-Impressionist Exhibition and who frequently encouraged artists to illustrate texts with lithographs, etchings and woodcuts.[1]

The old English practice of producing books with wood-cut or wood-engraved illustrations had enjoyed a revival at the end of the nineteenth century under the patronage of new private presses. It was on the Continent, however – and in Germany in particular – that the medium was vigorously embraced by modern artists. Kristian seems to have had some affinity with avant-garde developments in Munich before the war, and knowledge of graphic art by Kandinsky and Franz Marc. Certainly the abstract woodcuts he made at the Omega were more accomplished than any by his English contemporaries. The

1 See Judith Collins, *The Omega Workshops* (London: Secker & Warburg, 1983), p.116

Bloomsbury artists had almost no practical experience of printmaking. Vanessa Bell had produced one or two shaky silver-point etchings in 1905, but nothing since; and Duncan Grant had drawn a poster for the suffragettes and taken a hand in designing invitation cards for the Omega. Fry though, unrelenting as ever, immersed himself in the technical processes of printing: he took advice from J. H. Mason at the Central School of Arts and Crafts and employed Richard Madley, a professional printer whose premises were nearby, to produce his books. The third of these was Robert Trevelyan's translation of *Lucretius on Death*, for which Fry and Carrington collaborated on a woodcut for the title page, and the last, *Original Woodcuts by Various Artists*, the only publication by the Omega not to combine text and illustrations.

The suggestion for a folio of woodcuts came originally from Virginia Woolf in the summer of 1917. She and Leonard Woolf had just begun hand-printing their own stories for sale by subscription and were considering buying a press which would also reproduce illustrations. Vanessa Bell – now living with Duncan Grant at Charleston in Sussex and divorced from the day-to-day business of the Omega – responded eagerly to this casual invitation from her sister, and made plans to involve other artists in the project. But in September the idea was discarded when Leonard Woolf refused to concede final approval for the layout of the book. It was taken up the following year by Fry, who asked Simon Bussy, Mark Gertler, McKnight Kauffer and Edward Wolfe as well as Bell and Grant to contribute to a publication of woodcuts under the Omega imprint. (He also retrieved two unused prints by Kristian.) 'Roger I hear is cutting wood all over the carpets of Gordon Square,'[2] Carrington wrote to Virginia Woolf that autumn. Probably these artists were making woodcuts for the first time. 'We learned to do it ourselves', Grant recalled. 'I think Roger may have helped us at first. I found it very easy, but Nessa had difficulties at first. She kept gouging holes in herself.'[3] As well as the danger of self-mutilation, Bell and Grant suffered difficulties in acquiring the right tools from their isolated situation in the country. Perhaps unsure of their competence in wood-cutting, they both based prints on existing paintings. Vanessa Bell's *Nude* was made while she was working on a large decoration, *The Tub*, for which Mary Hutchinson had posed beside a tin bath. Reducing the scale by at least ten times for the woodcut enabled her to alter the proportions of the composition, resolving the awkward spatial relationship between the figure and the tub in the painted version and emphasising the prominence of the nude. Grant's woodcut of *The Tub* was copied directly from a painting of the same title and his *Hat Shop* was a witty reference to his own designs for hats to be sold at the Omega. Both artists' prints drew extravagant acclaim from Fry. Grant's he thought 'typical of what's best and most characteristic in him' in its fusion of formal coherence and delicate fantasy; and he told Bell: 'Your

2 Carrington to Virginia Woolf, [October 1918]: *Carrington: Letters and Extracts from her Diaries*, edited by David Garnett (London: Jonathan Cape, 1970), p.106

3 Quoted in Judith Collins, *op. cit*, p.163

4 Roger Fry to Vanessa Bell, 24 November 1918, *Letters of Roger Fry* vol.II, edited by Denys Sutton (London: Chatto & Windus, 1972), p.439

5 Judith Collins, *op. cit*, p.164

woodcut of the nude is simply lovely. I don't think I've ever admired you enough. I like it personally almost more than D.'s Hat Shop. It's really a big thing. You *are* an artist.'[4] The woodcuts in the Omega book are unrefined but effective, remarkably fresh and lively compared with the elaborate designs of many conventional printmakers: the artists 'shy away from ostentation of whatever skill they possessed'.[5] Their definite influence was from France, and particularly from Matisse – the pose of the nude in Bell's *The Tub* was taken straight from his *Le Luxe I* – and Derain, and their concern was similarly with surface sensibility. But set against the prints made by some of the Vorticists, and particularly by Edward Wadsworth (for whom the woodcut was a primary means of expression at this time), their form and structure is tame indeed. *Original Woodcuts by Various Artists* was published early in 1919 in an edition of seventy-five. It was the Omega's last communal endeavour. Financial failure and the strains of running the business almost single-handedly had worn Fry down. In June he announced a clearance sale, and then closed the shop.

After the demise of the Omega, Bell and Grant made only a few further experiments with woodcuts. Carrington, who had not been included in the Omega portfolio, found that the medium suited her well. Woodcuts were reasonably quick to do, and sold easily, and she had small blocks cut to her specifications locally. She printed a self-portrait in 1916, and in the next few years designed bookplates for Lytton Strachey and several of his friends. Unlike the Omega artists, Carrington did not rely on the obvious contrast of black and white for her effects, but was fascinated instead by the subtle interplay of light and dark in three tones which she realised through an arrangement of finely-graded lines. Her subjects were often derived from an earlier, pastoral tradition – the fall of Icarus, or a shepherd at rest in Arcadia. By 1919, however, she was beginning to think that woodcuts were 'too limited in their technique, & that certain elements, as colour, will never be able to be shown'.[6] Fry also continued to make woodcuts, and he too produced a self-portrait, as well as still-lifes and interiors in which he explored the formal possibilities of the medium. In 1921 the Hogarth Press published a dozen of his new prints. 'Roger again last night,' Virginia Woolf recorded in her diary that spring, 'scraping his woodcuts while I sewed; the sound like that of a large pertinacious rat.'[7] One hundred and fifty copies of *Twelve Original Woodcuts* were hand-printed by the Woolfs in November. They sold out within two days, and in the new year two further impressions were issued to meet the unexpected demand. It was one of the most successful ventures the Hogarth Press had yet undertaken.

6 Carrington to Mark Gertler, [January 1919], quoted in Jane Hill, *The Art of Dora Carrington* (London: Herbert Press, 1994), p.45

7 Virginia Woolf, diary entry 12 April 1921, *The Diary of Virginia Woolf* vol.II, edited by Anne Olivier Bell (London: Hogarth Press, 1978), p.109

The Hogarth Press was born on the dining-table of Hogarth House, the Woolfs' home in Richmond, in April 1917 following the impulsive purchase of a small handpress, an instruction booklet and some Caslon

Old Face type. It started as a hobby, but what had been intended as a therapeutic, manual occupation for Virginia Woolf soon mushroomed into a consuming and flourishing operation – an autonomous, un-demanding publisher of Woolf's own work and then a fully-fledged press whose eminence was widely acknowledged. It is remembered today, of course, for publishing for the first time in England Katherine Mansfield and T. S. Eliot, for the impressive list of other writers who appeared under its banner (among them E. M. Forster, Robert Graves, Christopher Isherwood, Rose Macaulay, Vita Sackville-West and H. G. Wells) and for its translations of the great nineteenth-century Russians and of the complete works of Freud. 'It sometimes happens,' one historian has written,

that a small, independent publisher, holding to high and exacting standards of intellectual content and aesthetic form, with only a secondary concern for making a profit, earns a secure reputation for publishing books that voice the foremost literary, social and political ideas of the day, a reputation that may go beyond even that enjoyed by larger and older houses. Such publishers were Leonard and Virginia Woolf at the Hogarth Press.[8]

8 Mary E. Gaither, 'The Hogarth Press 1917-1946' in J. Howard Woolmer, *A Checklist of the Hogarth Press 1917-1946* (New York: Woolmer Brotherson, 1976), p.3

Unlike many private presses founded in the slipstream of the pervasive Arts and Craft movement, the Hogarth Press was not concerned with *editions de luxe*; and it showed no interest in new experiments with typography. The Woolfs' intentions were more cerebral. Nonetheless they took some pleasure in the appearance of their books and care in the choice of artists they asked to decorate them. To begin with they relied mainly on their friends in Bloomsbury; later, when the Press became an established and profitable business, other designers were enlisted, notably John Banting (who drew covers for novels by Christopher Isherwood and Henry Green) as well as John Armstrong, McKnight Kauffer, Enid Marx, Robert Medley and Trekkie Ritchie. In the last years of the Press's independent existence (it was incorporated into Chatto and Windus in 1946) John Lehmann, who was then a partner in the business, introduced new artists associated with the neo-romantic movement, including Michael Ayrton, John Minton, John Piper, Graham Sutherland and Keith Vaughan.

Even before artists were asked to design dust-jackets, the earliest productions of the Hogarth Press were distinguished by their unusual covers. 'For many years,' Leonard Woolf remembered,

we gave much time and care to finding beautiful, uncommon, and sometimes cheerful paper for binding our books, and, as the first publishers to do this, I think we started a fashion which many of the regular, old established publishers followed. We got papers from all over the place, including some brilliantly patterned from Czechoslovakia, and we also had some marbled covers made for us by Roger Fry's daughter in Paris.[9]

9 Leonard Woolf, *Beginning Again: An Autobiography of the Years 1911-1918* (London: Hogarth Press, 1964), p.236

The Press's very first publication in 1917, *Two Stories* by the Woolfs themselves, contained four small woodcut illustrations by Carrington, which elicited praise from Lytton Strachey and aroused the immediate interest of Vanessa Bell. Despite the eventual abandonment of the woodcuts book, she was quick to volunteer a frontispiece illustration for Virginia Woolf's story *Kew Gardens* in the summer of 1918: 'It might not have very much to do with the text, but that wouldn't matter. But I might feel inclined to do the two people holding the sugar conversation.'[10] Again she relied on an earlier painting for inspiration: *A Conversation* of 1913, a portrait of three women gossiping at a window. However, when the story was published she was furious at the uneven printing of her block, which had been terribly over-inked in places. (The Woolfs' initial attempts at hand-printing were rather clumsy: they admitted to spoiling the edges of one of Carrington's woodcuts by chopping away at its margins with a chisel.) Virginia was stung by the ferocity of the criticism. Any ordinary printer could have done better in Vanessa's opinion, and she went as far 'as to doubt the value of the Hogarth Press altogether'.[11] The quarrel blew over, but might easily have erupted again when Bell's four woodcut illustrations to Virginia Woolf's collection of stories, *Monday or Tuesday*, were similarly disfigured by a commercial printer who impressed her blocks too heavily onto dreadfully poor paper. Still, when the following year the Woolfs decided for the first time to produce a dust-jacket, for *Jacob's Room* – the first of Virginia's novels to be published by the Press – they turned confidently to Vanessa Bell for the design. (Dust-jackets were not commonplace before the 1920s: until then, illustrated covers involved the laborious process of mounting four-colour prints on cloth cases.) It was, in fact, a collaborative effort: Vanessa made the drawing, Virginia chose the terra-cotta colouring, and Leonard Woolf advised alterations to the lettering. It was the start, though not a very auspicious one, of an important, successful and long-lasting partnership – the longest-lasting in the Press's history. The cover of *Jacob's Room*, a characteristically suggestive assembly of simple shapes – a table, flowers and curtains – was ridiculed by booksellers and buyers alike. It was quite unlike the linear, illustrative decorations to which they were used; 'it did not represent a desirable female or even Jacob in his room', Leonard Woolf explained, 'and it was what in 1923 many people would have called reproachfully post-impressionist.'[12]

Travellers for the Hogarth Press grew accustomed to the sniggering of bookshop assistants when they unpacked their wares for inspection. Reviewers found the look of the Press's books no less offensive: the *Star*'s remarked of Vanessa Bell's jacket for the first series of *The Common Reader* that 'only a conscious artist could have done it so badly.'[13] But Virginia Woolf never abandoned the partnership with her sister and during the next two decades Vanessa Bell produced dust-jackets for every one of her books, as well as designing the covers

10 Vanessa Bell to Virginia Woolf, 3 July [1918], *Selected Letters of Vanessa Bell*, edited by Regina Marler (London: Bloomsbury, 1993), p.214

11 Virginia Woolf, diary entry 9 June 1919, *The Diary of Virginia Woolf* vol.I, edited by Anne Olivier Bell (London: Hogarth Press, 1977), p.279

12 Leonard Woolf, *Downhill All the Way: An Autobiography of the Years 1919-1939* (London: Hogarth Press, 1967), p.76

13 Quoted in *The Diary of Virginia Woolf* vol.III, edited by Anne Olivier Bell (London: Hogarth Press, 1980), p.16 footnote 4

used for the Uniform Editions of her novels in Britain and America. (She also made drawings for the covers of the collections of Virginia's essays compiled by Leonard Woolf and published posthumously by the Hogarth Press.) Virginia Woolf's letters to Bell abound with enticements to illustrate her work, and with praise for her designs. 'Your style is unique; because so truthful; and therefore it upsets one completely',[14] she wrote after Vanessa sent her the jacket for *To the Lighthouse*. And Vanessa often admitted how moved she was by her sister's novels, and especially by their visual eloquence. As late as 1939, having read Virginia's story 'The Searchlight', she enthused: 'It seems to me lovely, only too full of suggestions for pictures almost. They leap into my mind at every turn. Your writing always does that for me to some extent.'[15] By that time Vanessa Bell's bold designs and lettering (usually in the lower case) had become a distinctive signature of Virginia Woolf's work –

14 Virginia Woolf to Vanessa Bell, [8 June 1927], *The Letters of Virginia Woolf* vol.III, edited by Nigel Nicolson, (London: The Hogarth Press, 1977), p.391

15 Vanessa Bell to Virginia Woolf, 31 May [1939], *Selected Letters of Vanessa Bell, op. cit*, p.454

the book, often the result of years of unremitting labour, anguish and exhilaration, and proffered to [the] public in trepidation, was protected and promoted by a cover that appeared to be the happy result of an afternoon's work in a summer studio with birds singing.[16]

16 Jane Dunn, *A Very Close Conspiracy* (London: Jonathan Cape, 1990), p.161

Vanessa Bell's book-jackets employ many of her favourite decorative motifs, familiar from her work in other media: flowers, curtains and circles and hoops, all images of plenitude and nourishment, merged into almost abstract patterns and often printed in a striking two-colour contrast. Many of her designs are, at most, only allusive to the title of the book and rarely do they indicate its contents. Once, when writing to John Lehmann to thank him for sending a dummy of one of her sister's novels, she admitted: 'I've not read a word of the book – I have only the vaguest description of it and what she wants me to do from Virginia – but that has always been the case with the jackets I have done for her'.[17] But this is not to suggest that they were necessarily produced on a whim: she filled a whole sketchbook with ideas for *A Room of One's Own* before settling on a simple design of a clock on a mantelpiece. Vanessa Bell's dust-jackets ranged from the purely abstract – a typically geometric combination of cross-hatching, circles and lines for Virginia's limited-edition essay *On Being Ill* – to the delightfully decorative – two flowers drooping from a vase for the first series of *The Common Reader*, a single rose for *The Years* – and the apparently descriptive – two ghostly figures on the shore, seen from a window ledge, for *The Waves*, an emblematic lighthouse for *To the Lighthouse*, three bank notes for *Three Guineas* (which Leonard Woolf considered the most beautiful of her designs). For *Walter Sickert: A Conversation* she provided a more elaborate set-piece drawing: a quite un-Sickertian still-life of fruit and drink on the table around which the conversationalists will dine. Virginia liked the cover so much she raised the price of her essay

17 John Lehmann, *Thrown to the Woolves* (London: Weidenfeld & Nicolson, 1978), p.27

on the strength of it. There is an attractive lightness of touch to all these; but, as Woolf's most recent biographer has suggested, in the late novels this tone is perhaps misplaced:

As Virginia Woolf's writing developed, the decorativeness of the covers became, to an extent, misleading: the heavy dark rose lying over the inter-locking circles on the cover of *The Years*, the pretty swagged floral curtain design for *Between the Acts*, make these novels look less powerful and angry than they are.[18]

However, more usually 'the perfect sisterly accord of writer and artist sharing the same vision'[19] was intuitively realised and this was exemplified in their most complete collaboration, the third edition of *Kew Gardens* published in 1927. Each of the twenty-one pages of Virginia's text is framed by the organic growth of Vanessa's designs, which allude to the light, shape and movement of the story, the spontaneity of the drawing echoing the flickering quality of the writing. Though the decorations shape the actual words of the story, they are imprecise enough not to overpower them. Yet they are so assured, Frances Spalding comments, as 'to make each page visually dramatic, text and image balancing each other as in Blake's illuminated books'.[20] 'God made our brains upon the same lines, only leaving out 2 or 3 pieces in mine,'[21] Virginia wrote teasingly to Vanessa after receiving her first illustrations for *Kew Gardens* – and later she asked, 'Do you think we have the same pair of eyes, only different spectacles?'.[22]

Vanessa Bell was the most prolific designer to work for the Hogarth Press, and she created what became almost its house style. With John Banting, she provided the designs used for the various series of pamphlets issued by the Hogarth Press in the 1920s and 1930s, which greatly enhanced the Woolfs' list of authors and contributed to the Press's growing prestige; and she drew jackets for novels by Henry Green, Edward Upward, Susan Buchan and others. She also supplied the emblem of a wolf's head used as the Press's colophon from 1925, apart from a brief period in the 1930s when it was supplanted by a more stylised device by McKnight Kauffer. Roger Fry produced a cover for William Plomer's *Paper Houses* and the Woolfs also published his *Sampler of Castille*. This was Fry's record, in words and pictures, of a journey through Spain in the summer of 1923. In each town he visited he jotted down sometimes amusing and always acute impressions of the Spanish people and their culture, and he made on-the-spot sketches which he later translated into careful illustrations of the places he described. Duncan Grant drew relatively few dust-jackets between the wars, though he decorated several covers for catalogues distributed by Francis Birrell's and David Garnett's bookshop in Bloomsbury. When Garnett invited him to design a cover for a new novel in 1931, Grant reminded him of the fate of his proposed jacket for Julian Bell's first volume of poems *Winter Movement*: 'Hatchard

18 Hermione Lee, *Virginia Woolf* (London: Chatto & Windus, 1996), p.369

19 John Lehmann, *op. cit*, p.26

20 Frances Spalding, *Vanessa Bell* (London: Macmillan, 1983), p.221

21 Virginia Woolf to Vanessa Bell, [7 November 1918], *The Letters of Virginia Woolf* vol.II, edited by Nigel Nicolson (London: Hogarth Press, 1976), p.288

22 Virginia Woolf to Vanessa Bell, [17 August] 1937, *The Letters of Virginia Woolf* vol.VI, edited by Nigel Nicolson (London: Hogarth Press, 1980), p.158

23 Duncan Grant to David Garnett, 28 October 1931; quoted in Frances Spalding, *Duncan Grant* (London: Chatto & Windus, 1997), p.316

said that he would tear off the one I did for Julian from every copy that entered his shop.'[23] Perhaps it was a fear of further retaliation from booksellers that led him to worry that his design the next year for Julia Strachey's story *Cheerful Weather for the Wedding* (a commission he inherited from Carrington after her suicide) was vulgarly put together; it was, in fact, one of his most fluent. Grant's easy draughtsmanship was particularly suited to graphic art: so, too, was his natural inventiveness. For Arthur Waley's translation of *Monkey* by the sixteenth-century Chinese writer Wu Ch'êng-ên he wound his drawing of a monkey around the entire book. The front half of the monkey's body filled the whole of the cover, and at the suggestion of the publisher David Unwin all the title details were put on the back, in keeping with the reverse nature of Chinese literature. This edition was published in 1942; when the Folio Society brought out a new one in 1968 Grant decorated the boards with a delightful freely-drawn pattern of lines and dots and inside contributed eleven black and white lithographs and one in colour, deliberately employing a Chinese style for some. In the last year of the war he made five vivid lithographic illustrations for a private edition of *The Rime of the Ancient Mariner* published by Allen Lane, and a little later dust-jackets for Dorothy Bussy's anonymous, but thinly-disguised, autobiographical novel *Olivia* and for her translation of Paul Valéry's *Dance and the Soul*. Grant readily agreed to produce a cover and chapter headings for a first novel by his friend Paul Roche, *O Pale Galilean*, and for his later books of poetry; and in the last decade of his life, with his enthusiasm for new projects undimmed, he adapted designs for early publications by Richard Shone and made a drawing (erroneously printed upside-down) for a small selection of poems by Peter Ackroyd.

In the 1930s Duncan Grant and Vanessa Bell were among the most prominent artists working in England. They were two of the first in a long list of names involved in that decade's most significant, and unexpected, development in printmaking. Britain already boasted, in McKnight Kauffer (actually an American by birth), the foremost poster designer of his age. Now, on the initiative of a handful of enlightened patrons – Jack Beddington at Shell-Mex (and later at J. Lyons), Frank Pick at London Transport and Stephen Tallents at the Post Office – the best contemporary artists were invited to produce advertisement posters for private and state businesses; and these were often also made available for sale to the public. This was one of the most important ventures in twentieth-century British advertising, in which a distinguished roll-call of designers participated: it included John Armstrong, Edward Bawden, Barnett Freedman, Tristiam Hillier, Paul Nash, Ben Nicholson and Graham Sutherland. Clive Bell, reviewing an exhibition of Shell-Mex posters at the Burlington Galleries in 1934, thought that the fuel company was 'likely to do more for English

24 Clive Bell, 'Shell-Mex and the Painters' in *New Statesman and Nation*, 23 June 1934, p.946

art in a dozen years than the Royal Academy has done in a hundred.'[24] He traced the origins of this movement to Fry's Omega Workshops twenty years before, which he considered the birthplace of a new school of applied artists; and so, unsurprisingly, he was one of the most vocal supporters of the art of poster-making. (He also sat, along with Kenneth Clark, on a committee to advise on the choice of artists to work for the Post Office.) Fry had hoped that the Omega's influence would infiltrate deep into ordinary lives; now billboard posters were everywhere hailed as an 'art gallery of the street'. 'For it is from posters and urban architecture,' Bell wrote in 1938

that the man on the bus is likely to get the bulk of his aesthetic experience – visual experience of course. Such architecture as might have delighted the eyes and raised the spirits of Londoners is being knocked from over his head as fast as picks and drills can do it, and is being replaced, for the most part, by what can only vex and depress. Posters, on the other hand, thanks almost entirely to these two beneficent undertakings [by Shell-Mex and London Underground], are daily bringing new motives of pleasure and surprise into the streets, and have, I believe, already raised perceptibly public, though not official taste.[25]

25 Clive Bell, 'Posters' in *New Statesman and Nation*, 9 July 1938, p.75

For the Shell scheme, Beddington commissioned paintings that celebrated the quiet charms of the English countryside and suggested the discoveries made possible by motoring, and which were re-produced by commercial lithographers as lorry bills to adorn the company's petroleum tankers. No one then thought the conjunction incongruous, and the project even received the support of the Campaign for the Preservation of Rural England. Vanessa Bell chose as her motif a picturesque view of the church at Alfriston, near Charleston, executed in a pointillist technique. Duncan Grant, too, depicted a landscape well-known to him, the bridge at St Ives in Huntingdonshire, close to David Garnett's home. For this, and for the four posters he made for the Post Office illustrating different types of workers – engineering workman, telephonist, postman, and telegraph messenger – and enumerating how many of each the GPO employed, he adopted an overtly naturalistic style. It had the explicit advantage of being easily legible. It also revealed how far removed he, and Vanessa Bell, now were from those artists who used poster-making as a means of educating public taste; and who, by introducing avant-garde compositions into the humble medium of the poster, prepared the way for their acceptance in the higher art of painting.

Most of these posters were translations from paintings commissioned specifically for that purpose, and some – such as Grant's still-life in the series with which Lyons decorated their tea-rooms – were simply reproductions of existing pictures. Commercial lithography remained an arcane process to many artists, and they gladly relied on lithographic technicians to interpret their designs.

26 Clive Bell, preface to the exhibition *Colour Prints by the Society of London Printmakers*, Redfern Gallery, London, 1948

Clive Bell was not alone in recognising the limitations of any form of printmaking which was not a direct expression of the artist's sensibility: he frequently urged painters to 'face for a moment the sound and fury of the shop'[26] and make at least their finishing touches on the stone. But more popular with many printmakers was the nineteenth-century method of working on prepared papers, which were then transferred to a zinc plate – and which did not require the original drawing to be made in reverse. Roger Fry discovered a shop that sold lithographic papers in Paris in 1927, and used them to execute a handful of farmyard scenes and landscapes, portraits of his mother and atmospheric interiors of French churches, which he included in *Ten Architectural Lithographs* published by the Architectural Press in 1930. There were one or two firms in the 1930s who sponsored the production of autolithography. In 1937 Robert Wellington of the Zwemmer Gallery (with John Piper as his technical adviser) set up Contemporary Lithographs Ltd which published two series of colour lithographs by various artists, the size of large decorative wall prints, and drawn directly onto the stones at the Curwen Press. The first series was intended for the decoration of schools, the second more generally for collectors with a modest income; and most artists chose suitably familiar, even juvenile, subjects. Vanessa Bell's *The Schoolroom* conformed very obviously to this prospectus; and Duncan Grant's *At the Ballet*, in which he played on the contrast in colour and movement of a troupe of brilliantly-lit dancers gliding above the heads of sedentary spectators, easily satisfied the demand for attractive and breezy images. Contemporary Lithographs received critical acclaim when the complete set was exhibited at the Leicester Galleries in 1938 (Clive Bell was again to the fore), but they did not sell to anything like the extent anticipated. Similar problems with distribution affected Everyman Prints, a scheme devised by the Artists International Association in 1939 – even though their lithographs were sold through high street retailers such as Marks & Spencer. The AIA, a communist-led co-operative organisation of which Bell and Grant were members and with which Quentin Bell was particularly involved, directed its activities towards working-class causes, touring its exhibitions to factory canteens and restaurants. Everyman Prints were to depict scenes of contemporary life, and Vanessa Bell's lithograph, *London Children in the Country*, was an image as current and as appropriate to its audience as possible, the arrival of the first evacuees from the East End.

Bell's and Grant's interest in lithography was encouraged by the French artist Pierre Clairin, a friend who was often their host in Paris. Clairin was a fastidious and knowledgeable printmaker (he was professor of lithography at the Ecole des Beaux-Arts) and his small and delicate colour lithographs can still be seen on the walls of

Charleston. And it was the French *peintre-graveur* example which Bell's and Grant's most surprising patrons – the Ladies of Miller's – hoped to emulate from an unlikely base in Sussex. The Ladies were Frances Byng-Stamper and Caroline Lucas, two genteel, well-to-do sisters with a passion for art, literature and music, whose ugliness was as unfortunate as their energy was astounding. In 1941 they opened a gallery in the old stables of their Georgian house, Miller's, on the High Street in Lewes, which they determined would flower as a regional centre for the arts. They shamelessly recruited any influential acquaintances to their crusade, and these included the nearby household at Charleston. 'The ladies' manners were exquisite,' according to their biographer, 'and they achieved their objectives by means of charming notes, persuasive telephone calls and invitations to tea.'[27] With the support of Maynard Keynes, its chairman, they secured the pick of the touring exhibitions organised by the Council for the Encouragement of Music and the Arts. They also put on shows with sculpture by Rodin, Maillol and Epstein and paintings by Bonnard, Picasso and Derain as well as a retrospective of the Omega Workshops; they published books, instigated lectures, concerts and a short-lived art school (at which Bell and Grant taught) and even made plans for a theatre. Clive Bell joked that Lewes had become one of the cultural capitals of Europe.

At the end of the war the indefatigable Ladies turned their attention to printmaking. In 1945 they were sent an exhibition by CEMA of European lithography from 1792 to the present day, and to it they added their own first publication, a portfolio of two lithographs each by Caroline Lucas herself, Bell, Grant and the South African-born painter Enslin du Plessis. The sisters bought their own press and invited a printer down from London to work with the artists; and they took scrupulous care pulling the prints and selecting handmade papers. The public, perhaps because it had been starved of the opportunity to buy similar work during the war, responded avidly and *Eight Lithographs* in an edition of one hundred, priced at £5 each, sold within weeks. Vitalised by this success, Miller's joined forces in 1948 with the Redfern Gallery in London (which, under the direction of Rex Nan Kivell, was the principal outlet for contemporary prints) to form the Society of London Painter-Printers. This held annual exhibitions of colour lithographs by a great range of artists – 171 were represented in the first show – including two, the bibulous and outrageous Scotsmen Robert Colquhoun and Robert MacBryde, whom the sisters took into their tender care in Lewes. Such operations required the extensive use of prepared transfer papers, which were sent either to the Chiswick Press in London or to the master printer Louis Ravel in Paris. Clive Bell, in his preface to the catalogue of the Society's first exhibition, noted the markedly different effects achieved by the two printers, preferring Ravel's grave, velvety richness, which

27 Diana Crook, *The Ladies of Miller's* (Lewes: Dale House Press, 1996), p.19

22

28 Vanessa Bell to Helen Anrep, 9 September [1949], *Selected Letters of Vanessa Bell, op. cit*, p.519

29 Vanessa Bell to Janie Bussy, 11 March 1945, *Selected Letters of Vanessa Bell, op. cit*, p.489

30 Jeanette Winterson, *Art Objects* (London: Jonathan Cape, 1995), p.123

aspired almost to the texture of a fresco, to the Chiswick Press's gaiety and lightness. Vanessa Bell, on a visit to Ravel in Paris the following year, agreed that 'the French print so much better than the English that I think it's worthwhile getting them to do it if one can produce enough French money to pay for it'.[28]

The sisters continued to commission portfolios which they promoted themselves, and they were ruthless in extracting work from any capable source. Vanessa Bell told Janie Bussy in France that prints were certain to be demanded of her the moment she crossed the Channel: 'I am sure lithos of Nice would sell like hot cakes. They can be either one, two three or even four colours. It's the kind of thing one can do sometimes when one hasn't time or materials for painting in oils.'[29] In 1948 Miller's published *Six Lithographs* by Vanessa Bell and Duncan Grant. Their prints for Miller's have an undeniable charm, largely because of their anecdotal matter. They appealed to the English preference for uncomplicated subjects with portraits of their grandchildren, still-lifes of flowers and fruit and images of domestic animals, always enlivened by their own unique decorative touches. In 1954 the Charleston artists' collaboration with the Ladies of Miller's was concluded when the Press was disbanded – and although after Vanessa Bell's death Grant accepted the occasional invitation to produce a lithograph and even one or two etchings, this effectively marked the end of their printmaking activities.

In the torrent of books and essays on the Bloomsbury artists over the last twenty years or so, scant attention has been paid to their graphic work. It constitutes, of course, only a fraction of their vast, and varied, output. Above all, it was ephemeral. Carrington's woodcuts were sometimes just slipped into an envelope with her letters. Bell's and Grant's posters were used in advertising campaigns which inevitably ran their course. The volumes of woodcuts printed at the Omega Workshops and the Hogarth Press were published in small editions; and, like the portfolios of lithographs from Miller's, many have subsequently been divided up. Unbroken examples are rarely affordable to private buyers – but one, the novelist Jeanette Winterson, has confessed the 'immediate bodily delight' a copy of Fry's *Twelve Original Woodcuts* gives her: 'Is it the hand-decorated coloured-paper wrappers, or the thick cream insides, or the fact that she [Virginia Woolf] stitched this book that I have before me now? It is association, intrinsic worth, beauty, a commitment to beautiful things, and the deep passage of the woodcuts themselves.'[30] Virginia Woolf's novels and essays were issued in far greater numbers, but only very few are found today with their jackets intact. Dust-wrappers were often thrown away, or they might be pasted to the inside covers. Even at Charleston, the house shared by Bell and Grant for fifty years, none survive; there they were quite as likely to become part of a still-life arrangement or, left lying around a studio, to be spattered with paint. Those that had not been vandalised in some way might be 'rescued' by keen and light-fingered bibliophiles – Cyril Connolly, when he was a neighbour and paid regular visits, was always a prime suspect. He certainly knew their collector's value. But their true import was registered elsewhere. The Bloomsbury artists were in no way pioneers of any form of printmaking. They rarely made prints for their own diversion, but they welcomed any commission that came their way. They approved any proposal to make their work cheaply and widely available and they never lost the conviction that art could brighten up the dreariest corner of everyday existence. A moment's cheer might be afforded by a poster on the side of a petrol lorry, an original lithograph on a classroom wall or a shockingly colourful cover among a uniformly dun display of new publications – so that the writer John Russell, for instance, still remembers 'the way that bookjackets by Vanessa Bell used to speak to us across a crowded bookshop'.[31]

31 John Russell, 'How it Strikes a New Yorker' in *Charleston Newsletter* 5 (Richmond: Charleston Trust, 1983), p.13

PLATE 1 Vanessa Bell cat.20

PLATE 2 Vanessa Bell cat.23

PLATE 3 Vanessa Bell cat.21

PLATE 4 Vanessa Bell cat.22

PLATE 5 Duncan Grant cat.80

PLATE 6 Vanessa Bell cat.10

Vanessa Bell

PLATE 7 Vanessa Bell cat.24

PLATE 8 Vanessa Bell cat.8

PLATE 9 Duncan Grant cat.79

PLATE 10 Duncan Grant cat.73

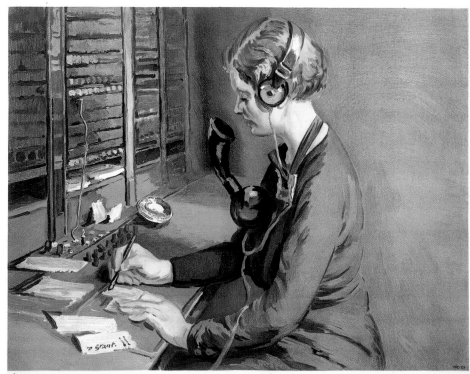

20,011 TELEPHONISTS

PLATE 11 Duncan Grant cat.82

PLATE 12 Duncan Grant cat.96

PLATE 13 Duncan Grant cat.97

PLATE 14 Vanessa Bell cat.17

PLATE 15 Duncan Grant cat.91

PLATE 16 Duncan Grant cat.102

PLATE 17 Duncan Grant cat.93

PLATE 18 Duncan Grant cat.103

PLATE 19 Duncan Grant cat.88

PLATE 20 Duncan Grant cat.104

PLATE 21 Roger Fry cat.153

PLATE 22 Duncan Grant cat.160

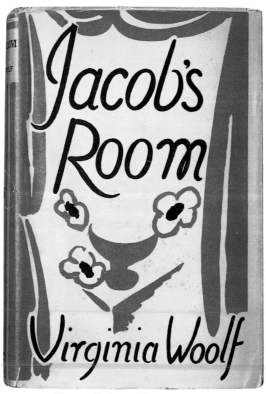

PLATE 23 Vanessa Bell cat.108

PLATE 24 Dora Carrington cat.146

PLATE 25 Vanessa Bell cat.115, 116, 112

PLATE 26 Vanessa Bell cat.111, 118, 121

PLATE 27   Roger Fry cat.150, 152, 151

PLATE 28   Vanessa Bell cat.144, 119

PLATE 29 Vanessa Bell cat.139, 145, 141, 140

PLATE 30 Vanessa Bell cat.130, 128, 120

PLATE 31 Duncan Grant cat.155

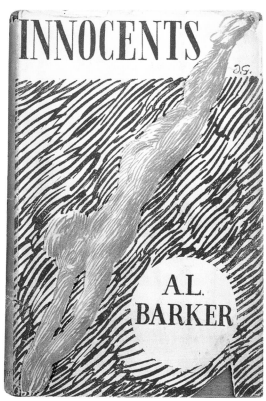

PLATE 32 Duncan Grant cat.156

PLATE 33 Duncan Grant cat.157

PLATE 34 Duncan Grant cat.163

PLATE 35 Duncan Grant cat.161

PLATE 36 Duncan Grant cat.164

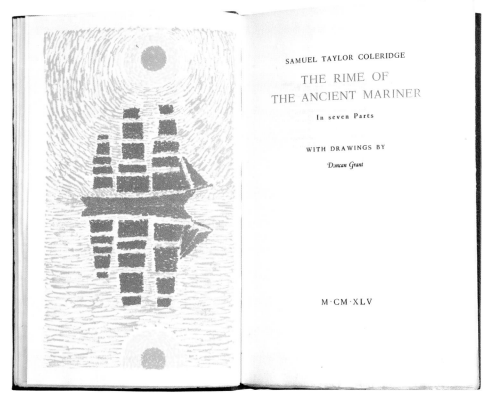

SAMUEL TAYLOR COLERIDGE

THE RIME OF
THE ANCIENT MARINER

In seven Parts

WITH DRAWINGS BY

Duncan Grant

M·CM·XLV

PLATE 37 Duncan Grant cat.85

In an
Eighteenth Century
Kitchen

ILLUSTRATED BY DUNCAN GRANT
PREFACE BY BEVERLEY NICHOLS

PLATE 38 Duncan Grant cat.169

Catalogue

I

Author's note

The compilation of a comprehensive catalogue of the
'multiples' produced by the Bloomsbury artists – the
woodcuts, linocuts, etchings, lithographs, dust jackets and
illustrations for books – has been a complex task. Apart
from J. Howard Woolmer's *Checklist of the Hogarth Press*
(an outstanding work of research to which I am indebted),
there has been little direct scholarship in any portion of
this area at all until, very recently, research into woodcuts
by artists associated with the Omega Workshops and the
Hogarth Press has been conducted by Jeremy Greenwood
(to whom I am grateful for an open, collaborative exchange
of information). Records of the 'multiples' in museums and
archives are sketchy and elsewhere there are few references
to these aspects of the artists' output, not least by the artists
themselves. However, from my vantage point as an art
dealer and bookseller specialising in the work of the
Bloomsbury Group, I have been in a unique situation to
put together this book of reference which hopefully will be
of value and interest to the many people around the globe
who are fascinated by the creativity that the Bloomsbury
Group brought to the world. The area of prints and book
design is just one aspect of that creativity.

Inevitably in this largely uncharted field, *The Bloomsbury
Artists: Prints and Book Design* will contain some errors and
omissions. I trust that any person who owns or uses this
book will recognise that; and I would welcome anyone
having relevant information making approaches through
the publishers or through The Bloomsbury Workshop in
London.

There are certain features of this volume which need to
be mentioned and these are dealt with below.

EDITION QUANTITIES

Where known the quantity produced of each edition of
book and print, as well as the publishers concerned, have
been noted; omission of this information means that it is
not determined.

The US editions of Virginia Woolf's books in some
instances carried Vanessa Bell's jacket designs. Although
on occasions the colours varied from the Hogarth Press
publications, these are essentially repeats of the earlier
issues and are consequently not listed.

SIZES

The sizes of books and prints are given in inches and
centimetres, height by width. Book sizes are for the front
panel, unless otherwise noted; print sizes are for the 'sight'
image, unless otherwise noted.

Section One
Prints and Illustrations for Books

Vanessa Bell

1 (previous page)
Dahlias
1918
Woodcut on white paper
From *Original Woodcuts by Various Artists*, published by the
Omega Workshops in an edition of 75 numbered copies
6⅛×4¼ in, 16.6×10.8 cm

2
Nude
1918
Woodcut on white paper
From *Original Woodcuts by Various Artists*
7¼×4¼ in, 18.4×10.8 cm

3
Kew Gardens
1919
Woodcut on white paper
Frontispiece for *Kew Gardens* by Virginia Woolf, published
by the Hogarth Press in an edition of about 170 copies and
hand-printed by Leonard and Virginia Woolf. *Kew Gardens*
was reprinted commercially in June 1919 (a month after the
first edition) in an edition of 500 copies
6⅛×4 in, 16.6×10.2 cm

4
Butterfly
1919
Woodcut on white paper
Tailpiece for *Kew Gardens*
This woodcut appears in three states:
(1) printed on the page
(2) printed on a separate piece of paper and pasted onto
the page
(3) printed on a separate piece of paper and pasted over the
original
2⅝×3⅝ in, 6.7×9.2 cm

2

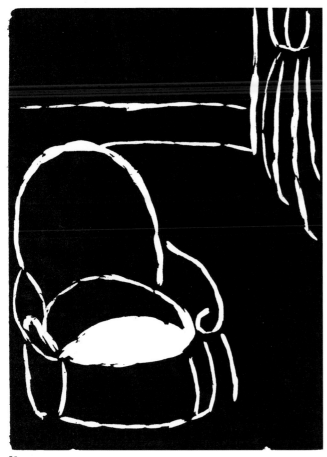

5a

5c

4

5
Illustrations for *Monday or Tuesday* by Virginia Woolf
1921
Published by the Hogarth Press in an edition of 1000 copies
Woodcuts on white paper
All images 5½ × 4 in, 14 × 10.2 cm
Images are to illustrate:
(a) *A Haunted House*
(b) *A Society*
(c) *An Unwritten Novel*
(d) *The String Quartet*

6

6
Wolf Emblem
The logo for the Hogarth Press used by the Press in most of its publications from 1925 onwards. Reproduced from the original ink drawing in various sizes but generally in the range of ¾ to 1¼ in, 1.9 to 3.2 cm diameter

7
Illustration for *The Legend of Monte della Sibilla*
by Clive Bell
1923
Published by the Hogarth Press in an edition of 400 copies and hand-printed by Leonard and Virginia Woolf. The still-life illustration from the original ink drawing by Vanessa Bell was also used on the front of the Hogarth Press's 'Autumn Announcements' catalogue, 1924 (see cat.110)
3¼×4¾ in, 8.3×12.1 cm

8 (PLATE 8)
Alfriston
1931
Lithographic coloured poster in six colours printed by 'McC and Co Ltd., Ldn' for Shell ('See Britain First on Shell')
30×44½ in, 76.2×113 cm (whole poster size)
Signed in the plate lower right

9
Illustrations for *Flush* by Virginia Woolf
1933
Collotypes from the original ink drawings on white coated paper
Published by the Hogarth Press in an edition of 12,680 copies with a second impression of 3000 copies printed in the same month (October) of publication
All images 7×4¾ in, 17.8×12.1 cm
Titles of images:
(a) *Miss Mitford Takes Flush for a Walk*
(b) *The Back Bedroom*
(c) *'So She Knitted and He Dozed'*
(d) *At Casa Guidi*
The Back Bedroom and *At Casa Guidi* are both signed in the plate lower right

10 (PLATE 6)
The Schoolroom
1937
Lithograph printed in four colours on white wove paper
Published by Contemporary Lithographs Ltd in an edition of 75-100 copies
18¼×24⅜ in, 46.4×61.9 cm
About 50 copies signed in ink lower right

11
Scene in a Post Office (not seen)
c.1939
Lithographic coloured poster printed for the GPO but never officially used
The likely reason that this image was not used was because the scheme was very short-lived; the advisory committee, which included Clive Bell and Kenneth Clark, resigned after disagreements with civil servants over the choice of artists
20×25 in, 50.8×63.5 cm

12
London Children in the Country
1939
Lithograph in black on white paper
Published by AIA Everyman Prints
11⅞×8 in, 30.2×20.3 cm
Signed and dated in the plate lower left
The image is believed to be related to the evacuation of children from London to country areas at the start of World War II

13
Amaryllis
1945
Lithograph in two colours on handmade white paper
From *Eight Lithographs*, published by Miller's, Lewes, in an edition of 250 copies
13⅝×10⅛ in, 34.6×25.7 cm
Signed in the plate lower right
Eight Lithographs was a collaboration between Vanessa Bell, Duncan Grant, Caroline Lucas and Enslin du Plessis to which each artist contributed two works

14
Girl Reading
1945
Lithograph in four colours on handmade white paper
From *Eight Lithographs*
13⅛×10⅛ in, 33.3×25.7 cm
Signed in the plate lower left

12

15
Child with a Book
1948
Lithograph in two colours on handmade white paper
13⅛×10⅛ in, 33.3×25.7 cm
From *Six Lithographs*, published by Miller's, Lewes, in an
edition of 100 copies
Signed in the plate lower left
Six Lithographs was a collaboration between Vanessa Bell
and Duncan Grant to which each artist contributed three
works

16
Roses
1948
Lithograph in three colours on handmade white paper
11⅝×8 in, 29.5×20.3 cm
From *Six Lithographs*
Signed in the plate lower right

17 (PLATE 14)
Child with Flowers
1948
Lithograph in two colours on handmade white paper
12×9 in, 30.5×22.9 cm
From *Six Lithographs*
Signed in the plate lower left

18
Church of the Gesuiti
c.1950
Lithograph in black on white paper
13⅛×8⅞ in, 33.3×22.5 cm

19
Flowers
c.1950
Lithograph in black on handmade white paper
Published by Miller's, Lewes
21×15 in, 53.3×38.1 cm
Signed in the plate lower right

20 (PLATE 1)
Flowers and Grapes
1951
Lithograph in four colours on white paper
10×7 in, 25.4×17.8 cm
Signed and dated in ink lower right

15

21 (PLATE 3)
Flowers in a Jug
1951
Lithograph in four colours on white paper
8¾×6⅛ in, 22.2×15.6 cm
Signed and dated in ink lower right

22 (PLATE 4)
Virgin and Child
1951
Lithograph in four colours on white paper
11⅛×7½ in, 28.3×19.1 cm
Signed and dated in ink lower right

23 (PLATE 2)
Basket of Fruit and Flowers
c.1951
Lithograph in four colours on white paper
9⅜×7¾ in, 23.8×19.7 cm
Signed in ink lower right

24 (PLATE 7)
Lady with a Book
c.1951
Lithograph in four colours on handmade white paper
20⅝×13¾ in, 52.4×34.9 cm
Published by Miller's, Lewes
Signed in ink lower right

Vanessa Bell

25

27

29

Dora Carrington

25
The Gravediggers
1917
Woodcut on white paper
Illustration for *Two Stories* by Leonard and Virginia Woolf.
Published by the Hogarth Press, 1917, in an edition of 150
copies and hand-printed by Leonard and Virginia Woolf
1⅝×3 in, 4.1×7.6 cm

26
The Servant Girl
1917
Woodcut on white paper
Illustration for *Two Stories*
1¼×3⅛ in, 3.2×7.9 cm

27
The Fireside
1917
Woodcut on white paper
Illustration for *Two Stories*
2×2½ in, 5.1×6.4 cm

28
Snail, The Mark on the Wall
1917
Woodcut on white paper
Illustration for *Two Stories*
2⅞×3⅛ in, 7.3×7.9 cm

29
Shepherd in Arcadia
c.1920
Woodcut on white paper
4¾×3¾ in, 12.1×9.5 cm

31

33

Roger Fry

30
Illustrations for *Polyphemus and Other Poems* by
R. C. Trevelyan
1901
11 illustrations, including one on title page, printed in two
colours to illustrate the poems. In addition, the title page
lettering is by Fry. Published by R. Brimley Johnson,
London
All illustrations 2½×4⅜ in, 6.4×11.1 cm

31
Still Life
1918
Woodcut on white paper
From *Original Woodcuts by Various Artists*, published by the
Omega Workshops in an edition of 75 numbered copies
7¼×4¼ in, 18.4×10.8 cm

32
Harliquinade
1918
Woodcut on white paper
From *Original Woodcuts by Various Artists*
Drawn by Mark Gertler but Fry physically cut the image
5⅜×5½ in, 13.7×14 cm

33
The Cup
1918
Woodcut on white paper
From *Original Woodcuts by Various Artists*
6×4¼ in, 15.2×10.8 cm

35

36

34
The Stocking
1918
Woodcut on white paper
From *Original Woodcuts by Various Artists*
7¼ × 4¼ in, 18.4 × 10.8 cm

35
Self-Portrait
1921
Woodcut on white paper
From *Twelve Original Woodcuts* by Roger Fry, hand-printed
by Leonard and Virginia Woolf at the Hogarth Press
November 1921 in a first edition of 150 copies; second and
third impressions printed on white coated paper were
published in 1922, totalling possibly an additional 200
copies
4 × 3¼ in, 10.2 × 8.3 cm

36
The Striped Dress
1921
Woodcut on white paper
From *Twelve Original Woodcuts*
5½ × 3½ in, 14 × 8.9 cm

37 (see page 52)
Still-life
1921
Woodcut on white paper
From *Twelve Original Woodcuts*
5½ × 4 in, 14 × 10.2 cm

38
The Grotto
1921
Woodcut on white paper
From *Twelve Original Woodcuts*
5½ × 3½ in, 14 × 8.9 cm

40

44

39
Ste Agnès
1921
Woodcut on white paper
From *Twelve Original Woodcuts*
5×3½ in, 12.7×8.9 cm
The image reproduces (in reverse) a 1915 painting *Figure Resting under a Tree, St Agnès*. The figure is that of Pippa Strachey

40
The Novel
1921
Woodcut on white paper
From *Twelve Original Woodcuts*
5½×4 in, 14×10.2 cm
The young man in the chair is believed to be Fry's son, Julian

41
Langle sur l'Anglin
1921
Woodcut on white paper
From *Twelve Original Woodcuts*
5×3½ in, 12.7×8.9 cm

42
The London Garden
1921
Woodcut on white paper
From *Twelve Original Woodcuts*
5½×4 in, 14×10.2 cm
The scene depicts the garden of Fry's home at Dalmeny Avenue, Highgate, London

43
Two Nudes
1921
Woodcut on white paper
From *Twelve Original Woodcuts*
5½×4 in, 14×10.2 cm

44
Interior
1921
Woodcut on white paper
From *Twelve Original Woodcuts*
5½×3½ in, 14×8.9 cm
The seated figure is that of Nina Hamnett

37

45

45
Dessert
1921
Woodcut on white paper
From *Twelve Original Woodcuts*
5½×4 in, 14×10.2 cm

46
Iris and Vase
1921
Woodcut on white paper
From *Twelve Original Woodcuts* by Roger Fry, hand-printed
by Leonard and Virginia Woolf at the Hogarth Press,
November 1921 in a first edition of 150 copies; second and
third impressions printed on white coated paper were
published in 1922, totalling possibly an additional 200
copies. This image, the last of the series, was used for the
covers of the second and third impressions (see cat.148)
4×3¼ in, 10.2×8.3 cm

47
Illustrations for *A Sampler of Castille* by Roger Fry
1923
Collotypes from the original pencil or ink drawings on
white paper
Published by the Hogarth Press in an edition of 550
numbered copies. All titles of the images detailed at the
base, as follows:
(a) *A Monastery, Segovia*
    7¼×5¼ in, 18.4×13.3 cm
(b) *Zaragoza*
    5¼×8 in, 13.3×20.3 cm
    Signed in the plate lower left
(c) *Calatayud*
    5¼×7 in, 13.3×17.8 cm
(d) *The park of Moncloa (Madrid)*
    5¼×8 in, 13.3×20.3 cm
    Signed in the plate lower left
(e) *Puente de S. Martin, Toledo*
    5¼×7 in, 13.3×17.8 cm
(f) *Escorial*
    5¼×7 in, 13.3×17.8 cm
    Signed in the plate lower left

47a

(g) *Segovia from Zanoramala*
    5¼×8 in, 13.3×20.3 cm
    Signed in the plate lower left
(h) *San Nicolàs, Segovia*
    5¼×7¼ in, 13.3×18.4 cm
(i) *Segovia Cathedral from the ravine of the Clamores*
    5¼×7¼ in, 13.3×18.4 cm
    Signed in the plate lower left
(j) *Outside Avila*
    5¼×7 in, 13.3×17.8 cm
(k) *Salamanca from across the Tormes*
    5¼×8 in, 13.3×20.3 cm

(l) *Ciudad Rodrigo from the Agueda*
    5¼×7 in, 13.3×17.8 cm
(m) *Zamora from the West*
    5¼×7 in, 13.3×17.8 cm
(n) *A Siesta, Zamora*
    5×8 in, 12.7×20.3 cm
(o) *Toro looking up from the 'trenches'*
    5¼×8 in, 13.3×20.3 cm
(p) *Toro looking down to valley of Duero*
    5¼×7 in, 13.3×17.8 cm

52

48
Portrait of a Man (not seen)
1923
Lithograph in black on cream wove paper
8×6 in, 20.3×15.2 cm
Signed and dated in the plate lower right

49
Cathedral with Square Dome
1927
Lithograph in black on cream wove paper
14¾×11 in, 37.5×27.9 cm
Edition of 50
Signed and dated in the plate lower left

50
St Jacques, Dieppe (interior of Cathedral)
1927
Lithograph in black on cream wove paper
21¾×14½ in, 55.2×36.8 cm
Signed, dated and titled in the plate lower right

51
Marseilles (church interior with spiral stair to pulpit)
1927
Lithograph in black on cream wove paper
14¾×10¼ in, 37.5×26 cm
Inscribed in the plate 'Marseilles' lower right
Signed in the plate lower left

52
Mariabella Fry
1927
Lithograph in black on same piece of cream paper as item below
7½×8⅛ in, 19.1×20.6 cm
Titled 'MF' and dated 'Aug 1927' in the plate lower left; signed in the plate lower right
This image of Roger Fry's mother varies slightly from the item noted below

53
Mariabella Fry
1927
Lithograph in black on same piece of cream paper as item above
8¾×7⅞ in, 22.2×20 cm
Titled 'MF' and dated 'Aug 1927' in the plate lower left; signed in the plate lower right

54
River and Trees
c.1928
Lithograph in black on cream wove paper
15×11 in, 38.1×27.9 cm
Signed in the plate lower right

55
Near Brantôme (river and trees)
1928
Lithograph in black on cream wove paper
14¾×11 in, 37.5×27.9 cm
Signed and dated in the plate lower left

56
Near Brantôme (trees, deckchair, roundhouse)
1928
Lithograph in black on cream wove paper
11¼×14¾ in, 28.6×37.5 cm
Signed and dated in the plate lower left

57
Near Brantôme (archway)
1928
Lithograph in black on cream wove paper
14½×11 in, 36.8×27.9 cm
Signed and dated in the plate lower left

56

58 (see overleaf)
French Farmhouse
*c.*1928
Lithograph in black on cream wove paper
11¼×15 in, 28.6×38.1 cm
Signed in the plate lower left

59
La Charité (buildings in a town)
*c.*1928
Lithograph in black on cream wove paper
11¼×13¼ in, 28.6×33.7 cm
Signed and titled 'La Charité sur Loire' in the plate lower
right

60
La Charité (interior of church)
*c.*1928
Lithograph on cream wove paper
18¾×12¾ in, 47.6×32.4 cm
Signed and titled in the plate lower right

58

61
Saint-Front, Périgueux
1930
Lithograph in black on cream wove paper
From *Ten Architectural Drawings*, published by the
Architectural Press Limited, London, in 40 sets, each set
signed and numbered by Roger Fry in ink inside front of
folder holding the complete set. In addition five sets were
made available for purchase by individual lithograph
14¾ × 11 in, 37.5 × 27.9 cm
Signed in the plate lower left

62
Baroque Altar, Perpignan
1930
Lithograph in black on cream wove paper
From *Ten Architectural Drawings*
15 × 11 in, 38.1 × 27.9 cm
Signed in the plate lower left

63
Notre Dame, Clermont Ferrand
1930
Lithograph in black on cream wove paper
From *Ten Architectural Drawings*
14¾ × 11 in, 37.5 × 27.9 cm
Signed in the plate lower left

64
Arles sur Tech
1930
Lithograph in black on cream wove paper
From *Ten Architectural Drawings*
15×11 in, 38.1×27.9 cm
Signed in the plate lower left

65
Rock-cut Church, Aubeterre
1930
Lithograph in black on cream wove paper
From *Ten Architectural Drawings*
14⅞×11⅛ in, 37.8×28.3 cm
Signed, dated ''28' and titled 'Aubeterre' in the plate lower left

66
Elne
1930
Lithograph in black on cream wove paper
From *Ten Architectural Drawings*
15×11 in, 38.1×27.9 cm
Signed and titled in the plate lower left

67
A Staircase, Narbonne
1930
Lithograph in black on cream wove paper
From *Ten Architectural Drawings*
14⅝×11 in, 37.1×27.9 cm
Signed in the plate lower right

68
Cluny Museum, Paris
1930
Lithograph in black on cream wove paper
From *Ten Architectural Drawings*
15×10¾ in, 38.1×27.3 cm
Signed in the plate lower left

69
Rock-cut Church, Saint-Emilion
1930
Lithograph in black on cream wove paper
From *Ten Architectural Drawings*
15×10⅞ in, 38.1×27.6 cm
Signed in the plate lower left

70

70
Trinity College Library, Cambridge
1930
Lithograph in black on cream wove paper
From *Ten Architectural Drawings*
12⅝×9⅜ in, 32.1×23.8 cm
Signed in the plate lower right

71
Scene on the banks of the Seine, Paris (not seen)
1930
Lithograph
9½×12½ in, 24.1×31.8 cm

72
Landscape with trees
*c.*1930
Lithograph in black on cream wove paper
9×13½ in, 22.9×34.3 cm
Signed in the plate lower left

Duncan Grant

73 (PLATE 10)
Musical Instruments for the Front
c.1918
Lithographic poster in four colours printed by David Allen
& Sons Ltd, 17 Leicester Street, London, WC1
30×20 in, 76.2×50.8 cm (whole poster size)
Signed in the plate lower right
Only three copies of this poster are known to exist, one in
the Victoria and Albert Museum

74
The Hat Shop
1918
Woodcut on white paper
From *Original Woodcuts by Various Artists*, published by the
Omega Workshops in an edition of 75 numbered copies
7¼×4¼ in, 18.4×10.8 cm

75
The Tub
1918
Woodcut on white paper
From *Original Woodcuts by Various Artists*
4¼×7¼ in, 10.8×18.4 cm

76
Illustrations for *The Legend of Monte della Sibilla* by
Clive Bell
1923
The book was hand-printed by Leonard and Virginia Woolf
at the Hogarth Press in an edition of 400 copies
Two illustrations, from the original ink drawings, are shown,
the frontispiece of courting couples (9¼×6¼ in, 23.5×15.9
cm) and an image of a reclining nude with lute (4×4¾ in,
10.2×12.1 cm). Both are signed in the plate

77
Decorations for *Poems* by G. H. Luce
1923
Published by the Hogarth Press
Two illustrations, from the original ink drawings, showing
hawks
8¾×5½ in, 22.2×14 cm
This book was first published in 1920 by Macmillan with
financial backing from Maynard Keynes. In late 1923 the
Hogarth Press purchased the remaining unsold sheets from
Macmillan and bound these with an eight-page signature
of preliminary matter including the two Duncan Grant
illustrations. The book was reissued again in 1924 in a very
similar format

74

75

76 78

78
Illustrations for *The Receipt Book of Elizabeth Raper*
1924
Frontispiece portrait of Elizabeth Raper, from the original
ink drawing, for *The Receipt Book of Elizabeth Raper*, edited
and foreword by Bartle Grant
Published by the Nonesuch Press, Soho, London, in an
edition of 850 numbered copies
3×2½ in, 7.6×6.4 cm
There are two further illustrations, from the original ink
drawings, a decorative design (3×2 in, 7.6×5.1 cm) and an
image of a couple on horseback (3×3 in, 7.6×7.6 cm)

79 (PLATE 9)
St Ives, Huntingdon
1932
Lithographic coloured poster in seven colours printed by
Vincent Brooks, Day and Son, London, for Shell
('Everywhere You Go You Can Be Sure of Shell')
30×44 in, 76.2×111.8 cm (whole poster size)
Signed in the plate lower right

80 (PLATE 5)
At the Ballet
1938
Lithograph in eight colours on white wove paper
18⅛×24 in, 46×61 cm
Published by Contemporary Lithographs Ltd in an edition
of 75-100 copies
Signed in the plate lower right

81
41,271 Engineering Workmen
1939
Photographic lithograph coloured poster printed for the
GPO
18×24 in, 45.7×61 cm
Signed in the plate lower right

82 (PLATE 11)
20,011 Telephonists
1939
Photographic lithograph coloured poster printed for the
GPO
18×24 in, 45.7×61 cm
Signed in the plate lower right

83
79,242 Postmen
1939
Photographic lithograph coloured poster printed for the
GPO
18×24 in, 45.7×61 cm
Signed in the plate lower left

84
7,681 Telegraph Messengers
1939
Photographic lithograph coloured poster printed for the
GPO
18 × 24 in, 45.7 × 61 cm
Signed in the plate lower right

85 (PLATE 37)
Illustrations for *The Rime of the Ancient Mariner* by Samuel
Taylor Coleridge
1945
Five full-page coloured lithographic illustrations (including
frontispiece) depicting scenes from the poem
Published by Allen and Richard Lane in an edition of 700
copies. Although dated 1945 on the title page, the book was
not issued until late 1946
All illustrations 9 × 5½ in, 22.9 × 14 cm

86
Partridge and Grouse
1945
Lithograph in black on handmade white paper
From *Eight Lithographs*, published by Miller's, Lewes, in an
edition of 250 copies
Signed in the plate lower right
13¾ × 10 in, 34.9 × 25.4 cm
Eight Lithographs was a collaboration between Duncan
Grant, Vanessa Bell, Caroline Lucas and Enslin du Plessis
to which each artist contributed two works

87
Window in Toledo
1945
Lithograph in four colours on handmade white paper
From *Eight Lithographs*
13½ × 10½ in, 34.3 × 26.7 cm
Signed in the plate lower left

88 (PLATE 19)
Persephone
1948
Lithograph in four colours on handmade white paper
Published by Miller's, Lewes
15½ in, 39.4 cm (diameter)
Signed in the plate lower right; signed in ink on the
surround lower right

89
Hawk (not seen)
1948
Lithograph in three colours on handmade white paper
From *Six Lithographs*, published by Miller's, Lewes, in an
edition of 100 copies
13⅝ × 10⅝ in, 34.6 × 27 cm
Almost certainly signed in the plate
Six Lithographs was a collaboration between Duncan Grant
and Vanessa Bell to which each artist contributed three
works

90
The Cat
1948
Lithograph in two colours on handmade white paper
From *Six Lithographs*
10 × 13 in, 25.4 × 33 cm
Signed in the plate lower left

91 (PLATE 15)
Collie Dog
1948
Lithograph in three colours on handmade white paper
From *Six Lithographs*
13 × 10 in, 33 × 25.4 cm
Signed in the plate lower right

92 (see page 62)
Venice
1949
Lithograph in black on white paper
16 × 22½ in, 40.6 × 57.2 cm
Signed and dated in the plate lower right, some copies also
signed in ink in the margin lower right

93 (PLATE 17)
The Harvest: Design for a Vase
c.1950
Lithograph in three colours on white paper
17¾ × 11 in, 45.1 × 27.9 cm

94
Two Women (not seen)
c.1950
Lithograph
Published by Miller's, Lewes (listed in an exhibition of
Miller's lithographs, Brighton Museum, 1954)

95
Girl by the Sea (not seen)
c.1950
Lithograph
Published by Miller's, Lewes (listed in an exhibition of
Miller's lithographs, Brighton Museum, 1954)

87

92

96 (PLATE 12)
Still Life
1951
Lithographic poster from a painting done by Grant in
Rome in the 1930s
38×29 in, 96.5×73.7 cm (whole poster size)
Published by J. Lyons & Co., printed by Chromoworks,
London
Grant's work was No.6 in this set of posters by well-
known contemporary artists (including John Piper and
L. S. Lowry) produced by J. Lyons for their own tea shops
and for purchase by the general public

97 (PLATE 13)
The Easter Bonnet
c.1955
Lithograph in two colours on white paper
9⅞×7 in, 25.1×17.8 cm
Signed in ink lower right

98
Illustrations for *Nurse Lugton's Golden Thimble* by Virginia
Woolf
1966
Six full-page lithographic illustrations depicting scenes from
the book
Published by the Hogarth Press, in an edition of 4000
copies
All images 5⅞×4⅜ in, 14.9×11.1 cm

99
Illustrations to *Monkey* by Wu Ch'êng-ên (translated by
Arthur Waley)
1968
Eleven full-page coloured lithographic illustrations
(including frontispiece) in two colours depicting scenes
from the book
Published by the Folio Society, 1968, in an edition of 2000
copies
All images 8¾×5½ in, 22.2×14 cm

98

99

100
Illustrations to *In an Eighteenth-Century Kitchen* edited by
Dennis Rhodes with a preface by Beverley Nichols
1968
Six full-page lithographic illustrations in black and white
illustrating various scenes in a kitchen. Also decorative end
papers (see cat.169)
Published by Cecil and Amelia Woolf, London, 1968
From the 2000 copies initially produced 1000 were issued
in hardback in 1968 and 500 in softback in 1983; the
additional 500 are expected to be published in 1999
All illustrations 8½×5 in, 21.6×12.7 cm

101
Field and Trees
c.1970
Etching on off-white paper
6×8 in, 15.2×20.3 cm

102 (PLATE 16)
Interior
1973
Lithograph in five colours on white paper
Published by the Penwith Society of Arts (printed by
the Curwen Studio) in an edition of 90, together with
two printer's proofs
14⅛×11⅞ in, 35.9×30.2 cm
Signed in pencil lower right
This work was included in a large portfolio of lithographs
by a variety of artists

103 (PLATE 18)
Washerwoman
1974
Lithograph in eleven colours on white paper
Published by Observart (printed by the Curwen Studio) in
a numbered edition of 350, with 10 artist's proofs, and
promoted through *The Observer* newspaper
29½×21 in, 74.8×53.2 cm
Signed in pencil lower right; editioned lower left

For Gladys W.
and Chicago (embraced).

Thirst into thirst two lovers pour
  Two longings in each other's phial
  Slaking self in the soul of each
Transposing fire in a blue-hot gaze
Till love has leapt from the heart of each
And both exchanged their lover's seat
So once again they are vials apart
And once again commute their hearts
To pour out selves in the glass of each
And fill two vessels with a single beat.

105

104 (PLATE 20)
Standing Woman
1974
Lithograph in nine colours on white paper
Published by Observart (printed by the Curwen Studio) in
a numbered edition of 350, with 10 artist's proofs, and
promoted through *The Observer* newspaper
30×17 in, 76.0×42.9 cm
Signed in pencil lower right; editioned lower left

105
Illustration for *The Kiss* by Paul Roche
1974
Published by the Keepsake Press in an edition of 180 copies
6½×10½ in, 16.5×26.7 cm (oval)

106

106
Salisbury Cathedral
1976
Etching
Published by Bernard Jacobson in a numbered edition of
100 copies
10½ × 13⅜ in, 26.7 × 34 cm
Signed and dated in the plate (printed in reverse) lower left;
editioned in pencil on the margin lower left and signed in
pencil in the margin lower right
This etching was hung, along with similar homages to
Constable by other contemporary artists, at the Tate Gallery
in 1976, at the time of a major Constable exhibition

Section Two
Book Jackets and Covers

Vanessa Bell

HOGARTH PRESS

107
Monday or Tuesday by Virginia Woolf
March 1921
Cover
1000 copies
7⅜×4⅞ in, 18.7×12.4 cm
This is a woodcut on paper pasted on to the front board of
the book

108 (PLATE 22)
Jacob's Room by Virginia Woolf
October 1922
Dust-jacket
1200 copies, plus 40 special copies for 'A' subscribers
(October 1922), 2000 copies (late 1922)
7½×5 in, 19.1×12.7 cm

109
The Legend of Monte della Sibilla by Clive Bell
December 1923
Cover (dust-jacket was plain wrapper)
400 copies
10¼×7 in, 26×17.8 cm
Note: 'With decorations and a cover design by Duncan
Grant and Vanessa Bell' is printed on the dust-jacket but
Quentin Bell in his *Bloomsbury* (Weidenfeld and Nicolson
1968) attributed the cover to Vanessa Bell alone. Only her
signature appears in the design

110
Autumn Announcements
Autumn 1924
Cover for a catalogue for the Hogarth Press
The still-life image on this cover is a repeat of an illustration
in *The Legend of Monte della Sibilla* (see cat.7)

111 (PLATE 26)
The Common Reader by Virginia Woolf
April 1925
Dust-jacket and cover to the same image
1250 copies
8⅝×5⅝ in, 21.9×14.3 cm

107

The Legend of
Monte della Sibilla
or
Le Paradis de la
Reine Sibille
Clive Bell

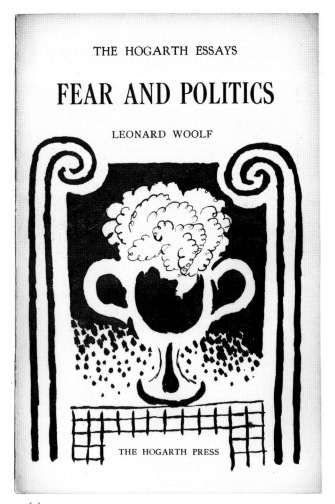

113(1)

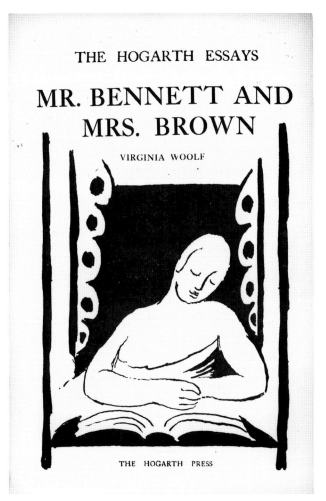

113(2)

112 (PLATE 25)
Mrs Dalloway by Virginia Woolf
May 1925
Dust-jacket
2000 copies (May 1925), 1000 copies (September 1925)
7⅜ × 5 in, 18.7 × 12.7 cm

113
The Hogarth Essays
Covers designed by Vanessa Bell. The First Series
comprised nineteen titles published in 1924, 1925, 1926.
In 1925 Bell's original cover design of a woman reading
a book was dropped and replaced by her design of a vase
of flowers. The Second Series contained 16 titles, published
in 1926, 1927, 1928, and used two different decorative
designs by Vanessa Bell. Only one title was published in the
Third Series (1937), using one version of the same cover
design as for the Second Series
First Series generally 8½ × 5½ in, 21.4 × 13.8 cm, but some
variations. *Second Series* generally 6⅝ × 4⅛ in, 16.6 × 10.3 cm,
but some variations. *Third Series* 6⅝ × 4⅜ in, 16.6 × 10.9 cm

114
Hogarth Stories
Decorative covers designed by Vanessa Bell. Two titles were
published in 1927
Generally 6¾ × 4¼ in, 17 × 10.6 cm

115 (PLATE 25)
To the Lighthouse by Virginia Woolf
May 1927
Dust-jacket
3000 copies (May 1927); 1000 copies (June 1927); 1500
copies (May 1928)
7⅜ × 4⅞ in, 18.7 × 12.4 cm

116 (PLATE 25)
Kew Gardens by Virginia Woolf
November 1927
Covers
500 numbered copies
9⅛ × 5¾ in, 23.2 × 14.6 cm
This, the third edition of *Kew Gardens*, was in a totally
different format to the earlier editions of 1919. In addition
to the cover, the title page and decorations to each page of
text were designed by Vanessa Bell

117
Hogarth Living Poets
Eight titles in the First Series, published in 1928 and 1929,
had covers to the same decorative design by Vanessa Bell
7½ × 5 in, 18.9 × 12.5 cm but some variations

118 (PLATE 26)
A Room of One's Own by Virginia Woolf
October 1929
Dust-jacket
3040 copies (October 1929); 3030 copies (November
1929), 3030 copies, 3050 copies (December 1929); 2500
copies (March 1930)
7 × 4½ in, 17.8 × 11.4 cm

119 (PLATE 28)
On Being Ill by Virginia Woolf
November 1930
Dust-jacket
250 numbered copies, all signed by the author
8 × 5⅛ in, 20.3 × 13 cm

120 (PLATE 30)
The Waves by Virginia Woolf
October 1931
Dust-jacket
7113 copies (October 1931), 4940 copies (October 1931)
7½ × 4¾ in, 19.1 × 12.1 cm

121 (PLATE 26)
The Common Reader: Second Series by Virginia Woolf
October 1932
Dust-jacket
3200 copies (October 1932), 1515 copies (November 1932)
8½ × 5⅝ in, 21.6 × 14.3 cms

122
Charles Lamb – His Life by Edmund Blunden
March 1934
Dust-jacket
1500 copies
8¾ × 5½ in, 22.2 × 14 cm

123

123
Walter Sickert: A Conversation by Virginia Woolf
October 1934
Cover
3800 copies
7¼ × 4⅞ in, 18.4 × 12.4 cm

124
Change Your Sky by Anna D. Whyte
March 1935
Dust-jacket
1200 copies
7¾ × 4⅞ in, 19.7 × 12.4 cm

126

125

125
The Funeral March of A Marionette by Susan Buchan
October 1935
Dust-jacket
1500 copies
7½×4¾ in, 19.1×12.1 cm

126
Chase of the Wild Goose by Mary Gordon
May 1936
Dust-jacket
1200 copies
8⅝×5½ in, 21.9×14 cm

127
Lights are Bright by Anna D. Whyte
October 1936
Dust-jacket
1219 copies
7×4½ in, 17.8×11.4 cm

128 (PLATE 30)
The Years by Virginia Woolf
March 1937
Dust-jacket
18,142 copies
7⅛×4¾ in, 18.1×12.1 cm

129
Journey to the Border by Edward Upward
March 1938
Dust-jacket
1200 copies
7½×4½ in, 19.1×11.4 cm

131

132

130 (PLATE 30)
Three Guineas by Virginia Woolf
June 1938
Dust-jacket
16,250 copies
7¼×4¾ in, 18.4×12.1 cm

131
Complete Catalogue of the Hogarth Press
Summer 1939
Cover
8⅜×5½ in, 21.3×14 cm

132
Amber Innocent by Joan Adeney Easdale
September 1939
Dust-jacket
1000 copies
8½×5⅜ in, 21.6×13.7 cm

133
Roger Fry A Biography by Virginia Woolf
July 1940
Dust-jacket. Oil portrait of Roger Fry (c 1925) by Vanessa
Bell reproduced in black and white
2530 copies (July 1940), 1130 copies (August 1940),
1010 copies (November 1940)
8½×5½ in, 21.6×14 cm

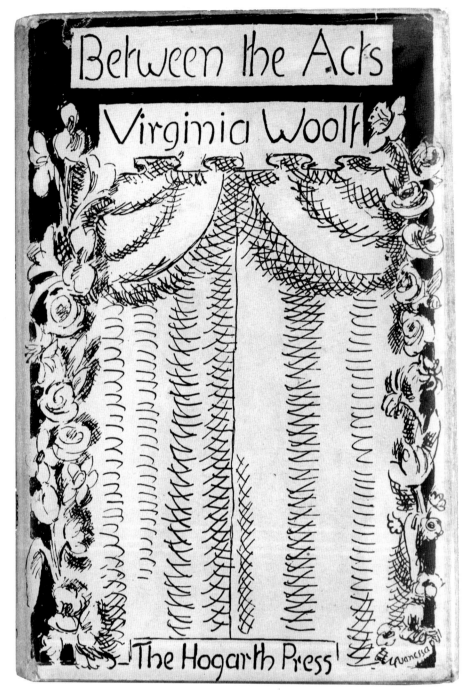

134

134
Between the Acts by Virginia Woolf
July 1941
Dust-jacket
6358 copies (July 1941), 4600 copies (July 1941), 2000
copies (November 1941), 3000 copies (January 1947)
7⅛×4¾ in, 18.1×12.1 cm

135

135
The Death of the Moth and other Essays by Virginia Woolf
June 1942
Dust-jacket
4500 copies (June 1942), 4600 copies (June 1942), 2000
copies (July 1942), 1200 copies (March 1945)
8½×5⅜ in, 21.6×13.7 cm

136

136
A Haunted House and other Short Stories by Virginia Woolf
January 1944
Dust-jacket
6000 copies (January 1944), 3000 copies (February 1944),
6000 copies (June 1944)
7¼ × 4⅞ in, 18.4 × 12.4 cm

137

137
Back by Henry Green (Henry Vincent Yorke)
November 1946
Dust-jacket
5000 copies
7¼×4¾ in, 18.3×12.1 cm

138
The Moment and other Essays by Virginia Woolf
1947
Dust-jacket
10,000 copies
8 × 5¼ in, 20.3 × 13.3 cm

139 (PLATE 29)
The Captain's Death Bed and other Essays by Virginia Woolf
1950
Dust-jacket
10,000 copies
8 × 5 in, 20.3 × 12.7 cm

140 (PLATE 29)
A Writer's Diary by Virginia Woolf (edited by Leonard Woolf)
November 1953
Dust-jacket
9000 copies (November 1953), 5250 copies (December 1953)
9 × 5¾ in, 22.9 × 14.6 cm

141 (PLATE 29)
Granite and Rainbow by Virginia Woolf
1958
Dust-jacket
6000 copies
8¾ × 5½ in, 22.2 × 14 cm

142
Dust-jackets to the Uniform Edition of many of Virginia Woolf's works in a standard design by Vanessa Bell in yellow and red-brown were published by the Hogarth Press in several printings from about 1960 onwards
8 × 5¼ in, 20.3 × 13.3 cm

138

OTHER PUBLISHERS

143
The Hogarth Essays
1928
Dust-jacket and cover (the cover design was a smaller version of the central motif on the dust-jacket)
Published by Doubleday, Doran & Company, New York
8¼ × 5⅝ in, 21 × 14.3 cm

144 (PLATE 28)
Poems of Mallarmé translated by Roger Fry and with commentaries by Charles Mauron
1938
Dust-jacket
1000 copies
Published by Chatto and Windus
8⅜ × 5¼ in, 21.3 × 13.3 cm

142

143

145 (PLATE 29)
Virginia Woolf and Lytton Strachey Letters edited by
Leonard Woolf and James Strachey
1956
Dust-jacket
4000 copies
Published by The Hogarth Press and Chatto and Windus
8¾ × 5¾ in, 22.2 × 14.6 cm

HOGARTH PRESS

147
Lucretius on Death, translation by R. C. Trevelyan
1917
Cover
Published by the Omega Workshops, London, with title
page to the same design on the cover
11¼×9 in, 28.6×22.9 cm
This woodcut was a collaboration between Carrington and
Fry but Carrington was responsible for cutting the block.

146 (PLATE 24)
Stories of the East by Leonard Woolf
April 1921
Cover
300 copies
8×4⅞ in, 20.3×12.4 cm
This is a woodcut imprint (in red)

LUCRETIUS
ON DEATH

BEING A TRANSLATION OF
BOOK III LINES 830 TO 1094 OF
THE DE RERUM NATURA, BY
ROBERT CALVERLEY
TREVELYAN

LONDON
PUBLISHED BY THE
OMEGA WORKSHOPS LTD
33 FITZROY SQW
1917

147

Roger Fry

HOGARTH PRESS

148
Twelve Original Woodcuts by Roger Fry
1922
Cover
Possibly 200 copies in total for the second and third
impressions of this publication were published with this
cover (the first edition was published in a hand-coloured
paper cover in 1921), all hand-printed by Leonard and
Virginia Woolf. The image was *Iris and Vase*, the last
woodcut in the first edition (see cat.46)
9×6½ in, 22.9×16.5 cm

149
A Sampler of Castille by Roger Fry
November 1923
Dust-jacket and cover to the same image
550 numbered copies
11¾×9 in, 29.8×22.9 cm

150 (PLATE 27)
Cézanne A Study of his Development by Roger Fry
November 1927
Dust-jacket and cover to the same image
1500 copies (a second impression was printed in 1932;
number of copies printed not known)
10×7⅜ in, 25.4×18.7 cm

151 (PLATE 27)
Paper Houses by William Plomer
February 1929
Dust-jacket
1262 copies
7½×4⅞ in, 19.1×12.4 cm

OTHER PUBLISHERS

152 (PLATE 27)
Flemish Art by Roger Fry
1927
Cover
Published by Chatto and Windus
2000 copies
10⅛×7⅝ in, 25.7×19.4 cm

153 (PLATE 21)
Mount Peacock by Marie Mauron (translation by
F.L.Lucas)
1934
Dust-jacket
Published by Cambridge University Press
7½×5 in, 19.1×12.7 cm

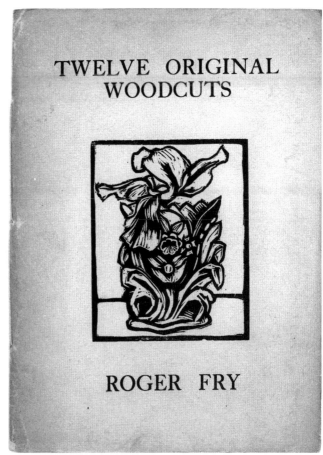

148

149

Duncan Grant

154
Living Painters Duncan Grant by Roger Fry
February 1924
Dust-jacket and cover to the same image
400 copies; a further 610 in a stiff paper cover to the same
design were published in 1930
10×7⅝ in, 25.4×19.4 cm

155 (PLATE 31)
Cheerful Weather for the Wedding by Julia Strachey
September 1932
Dust-jacket
1212 copies
7½×4¾ in, 19.1×12.1 cm
In the possession of the British Library there is a rough
sketch by Carrington for the cover of this book. It seems
quite possible that the project was taken on by Duncan
Grant after Carrington's death in early 1932

156 (PLATE 33)
Innocents by A. L. Barker
1947
Dust-jacket
3000 copies
7½×5 in, 19.1×12.7 cm

157 (PLATE 32)
Olivia by Olivia (Dorothy Bussy)
1949
Dust-jacket
3000 copies
8¼×5½ in, 21×14 cm

158
The Diary of Virginia Woolf, Volume I, edited by
Anne Olivier Bell
1977
Dust-jacket
15,000 copies
9¼×6¼ in, 23.5×15.9 cm

159
The Diary of Virginia Woolf, Volume II, edited by
Anne Olivier Bell
1978
Dust-jacket
8500 copies
9¼×6¼ in, 23.5×15.9 cm

154

OTHER PUBLISHERS

160 (PLATE 23)
Second Post-Impressionist Exhibition Catalogue
1912
Cover
Published by Ballantyne & Company, London
Published in four states; some editions contained
reproductions and the sizes of the catalogue varied
The figurative design was conceived by Roger Fry and
Vanessa Bell, but drawn by Duncan Grant, for a poster for
the exhibition; the design was then utilised for the cover for
the catalogue

DANCE
AND
THE SOUL

PAUL VALERY

*The original French text
with a translation by*

DOROTHY BUSSY

THE DIARY OF
VIRGINIA WOOLF

162

158

161 (PLATE 35)
Monkey by Wu Ch'êng-ên (translation by Arthur Waley)
1942
Dust-jacket
Published by George Allen and Unwin, London
8¾ × 13⅜ in, 22.2 × 34 cm (jacket design extends to the back
of the book)
The title page of this book depicts a drawing by Duncan
Grant of a monkey and a snake

162
Dance and the Soul by Paul Valéry (translation by Dorothy
Bussy)
1951
Dust-jacket
Published by John Lehmann, London
9¾ × 5½ in, 24.8 × 14 cm

163 (PLATE 34)
O Pale Galilean by Paul Roche
1954
Dust-jacket
Published by Harvill Press, London
7⅜ × 5 in, 18.7 × 12.7 cm
This book also contains vignette chapter headings by
Duncan Grant

164 (PLATE 36)
Monkey by Wu Ch'êng-ên (translation by Arthur Waley)
1958
Covers (designs on front and back)
Published by the Folio Society, London
2000 copies
9 × 4¾ in, 22.9 × 12.1 cm (both front and back)

165
To the Lighthouse by Virginia Woolf
1964
Cover
Published by Penguin Modern Classics (in association with
the Hogarth Press)
7¼×4½ in, 18.4×11.4 cm

166
A Smell of Burning by Margaret Lane
1965
Dust-jacket
Published by Hamish Hamilton, London
7¾×5⅝ in, 19.7×14.3 cm

167
All Things Considered by Paul Roche
1966
Dust-jacket
Published by Gerald Duckworth & Co, London
7½×5 in, 19.1×12.7 cm
The frontispiece of this book reproduces the portrait of the
author on the dust-jacket

168
Lytton Strachey: Volume One 1880-1910 by Michael Holroyd
1967
Dust-jacket (illustration of Strachey on the back panel of
the jacket)
Published by Heinemann, London
10×6½ in, 25.4×16.5 cm
The drawing of Lytton Strachey depicts him as a young
man. The work was specially commissioned by the author
for the jacket of his book and was drawn by Duncan Grant
in 1966 from an early photograph of Strachey

167

169 (PLATE 38)
In an Eighteenth-Century Kitchen edited by Dennis Rhodes
and with a preface by Beverley Nichols
1968
Dust-jacket and cover to the same design
Published by Cecil and Amelia Woolf, London
From the 2000 copies initially produced, 1000 were issued
in hardback in 1968 and 500 in softback in 1983; the
additional 500 are expected to be published in 1999
8¾×11½ in, 22.2×29.2 cm (jacket design extends to the
back of the book)
The book also contains endpapers to a decorative design by
Duncan Grant (see also cats 100, 173)

170
A Domestic Animal by Francis King
1969
Dust-jacket
Published by Longmans, London
8×5½ in, 20.3×14 cm
Although dated 1969 it was actually published in 1970,
delayed due to the threat of a libel action. The dust-jacket
reproduces a Grant gouache of a male nude (in a private
collection) not specifically produced as a jacket design for
this book

171
Enigma Variations And by Paul Roche
1974
Dust-jacket to a design by Duncan Grant but physically
executed by Richard Shone; some copies published in soft
cover
Published by The Thornhill Press, Gloucester
8⅝×6¼ in, 21.9×15.9 cm

168

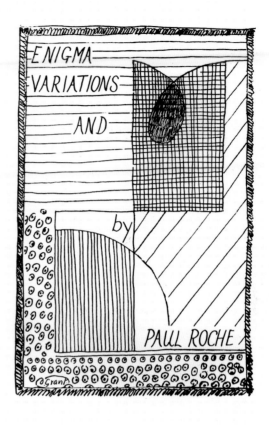

171

172

172
London Lickpenny by Peter Ackroyd
1973
Dust-jacket (design inadvertently printed upside down)
Published by the Ferry Press, London
500 copies (26 signed by the author)
9½ × 12½ in, 24.1×31.8 cm (jacket design extends to the
back of the book)

173
*Bloomsbury Portraits: Vanessa Bell, Duncan Grant and their
Circle* by Richard Shone
1976
Decorative cover adapted from the design for endpapers to
In an Eighteenth-Century Kitchen (see cat.169)
Published by Phaidon Press, Oxford
5000 copies
9¾ ×8½ in, 24.8×21.6 cm

Section Three
Ephemeral Items

Vanessa Bell

Omega Workshops Items
Vanessa Bell produced various items of an ephemeral nature for the Omega Workshops including a decorated menu card for a dinner for the early participants in June 1913

Christmas Cards
Throughout her life Vanessa Bell liked to send her friends 'home-made' Christmas cards and there are a number of examples of stencils and linocuts that she used at various times for this purpose

Woodcut
One example exists of a woodcut made by Vanessa Bell showing three people round a table on which is a teapot and cups. Probably executed around 1918

Chelsea Book Club Broadside No.1
A single page extract from Virginia Woolf's *The Mark on the Wall* incorporating two woodcuts by Vanessa Bell. Produced in 1921, 13¼ × 7⅛ in, 33.7 × 18.1 cm

The Son of Heaven
Programme cover for a play by Lytton Strachey, Scala Theatre, London, 1928. Two-colour design incorporating Chinese characters

Bookplate for Leonard Woolf
Line block print from original ink drawing
c.1925, 1⅓ × 4 in, 3.4 × 10.2 cm

Bookplate for Leonard Woolf

Trade Card for Phyllis Keyes Pottery
A trade card (black and green on cream) bearing the notice 'Phyllis Keyes Pottery, 29A Clipstone Street, Great Portland Street, London W1. Museum 5729'. Produced c.1930, 4 × 5 in, 10.2 × 12.7 cm

Illustrations for *Emlycaunt*
In the 1930s there appeared the possibility of the Hogarth Press producing a volume of the unpublished *Emlycaunt* by Julia Stephen to include illustrations by Vanessa Bell. Watercolours of scenes from the children's story were executed by Bell but no publication emerged. Around 1980 a quantity of the drawings were purchased by the Holland Library, Washington State University; the story itself was printed for the first time in *Julia Duckworth Stephen: Stories for Children, Essays for Adults* edited by Diane F. Gillespie and Elizabeth Steele (Syracuse 1987) with some of these illustrations reproduced in black and white

Basket of Flowers
Linocut to which the artist affixed tear-off calendars to distribute as Christmas gifts. 1950s, 6½ × 4¼ in, 16.5 × 10.8 cm

Dora Carrington

Book Illustrations
Carrington contributed a line drawing of *The Ouse, Bedford* and another of *Bedford High School* to the *Memoirs and Poems of A. W. St C. Tisdall* in 1916 and five line drawings for a school edition of *Don Quixote* published by Oxford University Press in 1922

Bookplates
Bookplates (mainly woodcuts) were made from 1917 to the mid 1920s for the following people:
St John Hutchinson
Lytton Strachey (several variants)
Montague Shearman
Lambert Bayne
Neil Little
Alan S. MacIver
Edith E. MacIver
G. Cecil Stevens

Self-Portrait
1916
Woodcut on white paper
1¾ × 1⅝ in, 4.4 × 4.1 cm
Two variants of this image exist

Honey Label Design
1917
A line block from a pen drawing, the label was made for David Garnett, then living at Charleston but working on the land as a conscientious objector

Woodcuts
Further woodcuts executed from 1917 to the mid 1920s exist, including *Cat* (two versions) and *Greyhound* (Jasper, Carrington's dog). Woodcuts were sometimes just an enclosed addition to Carrington's letters

Bookplate for Lytton Strachey

Honey Label

Roger Fry

Book Design
The title page of *From Whitechapel to Camelot* by
C. R. Ashbee (published by the Guild of Handicraft,
London, 1892) states 'Illustrated by M-or-N'. The copy in
King's College, Cambridge is inscribed 'To my dear Mother
from the Illustrator' in Fry's handwriting. No explanation
has been found for the initials 'M-or-N' on the title page;
the title page and seven full page illustrations appear to be
by Fry

The title page of *In a Garden & Other Poems* by
H. C. Beeching (published by John Lane, The Bodley
Head, 1895), was designed by Fry

Fry designed the endpapers (executed by Winifred Gill)
and probably the design on the front cover for *The Celestial
Omnibus and other Stories* by E. M. Forster (published by
Sidgwick and Jackson, 1911)

Christmas Cards
A card was designed by Fry for Christmas 1911 (the
woodcut was made by Winifred Gill). In a letter to his
mother enclosed with the card Fry said 'It's missed a little
in places but then it don't pretend to be anything but a
reminder and carrier of good wishes'

A woodcut Christmas card was made by Fry for the Omega
Workshops, 1913. There is record of a further woodcut
Christmas card made for Agnes Fry around 1913. Part of
this image, a basket of flowers, was apparently later
detached, presumably for employment elsewhere.
A woodcut landscape was also made

Omega Workshops Items
Roger Fry produced several notices for Omega Workshops
exhibitions including a poster for 'Modern Paintings,
Dresses and Pottery' in 1918. He collaborated with
Carrington to produce the cover for the Omega Workshops
publication *Lucretius on Death* (1917) and cut the wood-
block for the Omega Workshops device on the title page of
Original Woodcuts by Various Artists (1918)

London Group Exhibition Catalogue
A still-life design believed to be by Fry was used for the
cover of the 1928 exhibition catalogue. The motif was used
again for an exhibition which took place late in 1934, not
long after Fry's death, which tends to confirm the design is
by him

Poster for Roger Fry Lecture on Watteau and Chardin
Lithograph, 20×14 in, 50.8×35.6 cm, printed by Emberlin
& Son, Oxford, 1932

Title page

Mr ROGER FRY
will give a lecture on
WATTEAU &
CHARDIN
in the
HALL of
UNIVERSITY
COLLEGE
on MONDAY
JAN 18th
at
8·30 P.M.

Sir MICHAEL SADLER
has kindly consented to take the
chair.

EMBERLIN & SON, 15 THE BROAD, OXFORD 1932

Poster 1932

Duncan Grant

Suffragette Poster
Duncan Grant designed a poster in support of the suffragette movement, *c*.1909

Linocut
An example of a linocut of a prancing horse, 1913-14, is to be found at Charleston. This is the only known copy of the image

Omega Workshops Items
Duncan Grant produced the Omega Workshops opening invitation card and later a number of designs to promote Omega Workshops exhibitions, as well as a Christmas card. Amongst these designs was a woodcut cover to an exhibition catalogue of sketches by M. Larionov and drawings by the girls of the Dudley High School, 1918

Catalogue cover 1921

Fanfare: A Musical Causerie
Cover design for a magazine. Seven fortnightly issues
appeared between October 1921 and January 1922

Some Contemporary English Artists
Cover design to a catalogue containing 22 black and white
reproductions issued by Birrell and Garnett, London, 1921

A Catalogue of Secondhand English and Foreign Books (No.2)
Cover to a catalogue issued by Birrell and Garnett, London,
1921

Catalogue of Secondhand Books
Cover design and lettering to a catalogue issued by Birrell
and Garnett, London c.1922

Design
Cover decoration for a magazine entitled *Design*, c.1925.
Grant's image, however, was not utilised

Poster for Vanessa Bell Exhibition
A poster was designed for Vanessa Bell's exhibition at the
Cooling Galleries, 1930

Books of the Month
Cover design for booksellers Simpkin Marshall (1941) Ltd,
Rossmore Court, Park Road, London NW1
Dated 'December 1945', 8½×5½ in, 21.6×14 cm

The Arts
Various cover design alternatives were produced by Grant
in 1946 but the magazine disbanded before any of his
images were used. The first number carried a poem *Europa
and the Bull* which Grant illustrated

West Firle
Cover illustration (reproducing a pencil drawing of the
church) for a leaflet, 1950s, containing a history of the
village and surrounding area written by Viscount Gage and
commissioned by the West Firle Church Council

Firle Place Brochure
Grant produced several designs for a brochure for Firle
Place (the stately home close to Charleston) in the 1950s
but it is not established if these were used

Wedding Dinner Invitation
On the occasion of the marriage of Derry Moore to
Eliza Lloyd, 1968, Grant illustrated the invitation with
a decorative border of sheaves of corn

The Berwick Church Paintings by Richard Shone
(see overleaf)
Cover illustration for the publication published by the
Towner Art Gallery, Eastbourne, for the exhibition of
Berwick Church paintings, July 1969
6½×7 in, 16.5×19.4 cm

Duncan Grant: Watercolours and Drawings
Cover to a d'Offay Couper Gallery exhibition catalogue,
1972. The design was the same as that of Birrell's and
Garnett's *Some Contemporary English Artists* with only the
lettering, in the hand of Duncan Grant, altered

Don Giovanni Programme
Illustration to the programme of *Don Giovanni* performed
at Glyndebourne,1977

Catalogue cover 1972, reusing 1921 design

THE BERWICK CHURCH PAINTINGS

Cover illustration 1969

Author's acknowledgements

I am most appreciative of the permissions granted by
the copyright holders of the estates of Vanessa Bell, Dora
Carrington, Roger Fry and Duncan Grant to reproduce
the work of these artists.

In addition, thanks are due to the publishers Cambridge
University Press, Chatto and Windus, Heinemann, Allen
Lane and Cecil Woolf, for permission to reproduce book
jackets and illustrations and to The Shell Art Collection
at the National Motor Museum, Beaulieu, and the GPO
for permission to reproduce posters.

Apart from the people and organisations noted above,
I am most grateful to the following who have assisted me
in various ways with this catalogue:

Richard Shone (pre-eminent in his knowledge of
Bloomsbury art), Regina Marler, Frances Spalding, Robert
Reedman, Robert Brandeis, Carmen Socknat (a tireless
and dedicated librarian, with Dr Brandeis, at Victoria
University, Toronto), Sue Fox (for research conducted at
the Berg Collection, New York Public Library), Gordon
Samuel, Paul Roche, Abigail Willis (who indefatigably typed
and retyped the manuscript), Jane Hill, Rosemary Evison,
Erika Ingham, Polly McAndrew, Jacky Cox (Modern
Archivist at Kings College, Cambridge), Craufurd and
Nancy Goodwin, Michael Metcalfe, Clarissa Roche, Lester
and Eileen Traub, Marcia Stather and Colin Mills (for the
photographs).

I am also most grateful to Angelica Garnett and James
Beechey who wrote the foreword and introduction
respectively; both pieces are significant contributions to
this book.

Index of works catalogued

References are to catalogue numbers and colour plates. Black and white illustrations accompany many of the catalogue entries.

94

Duncan Grant